Devotional

ACTIVITIES FOR KIDS

Writer
Marilyn Schneider

Artist
Angela Owens

Unless otherwise marked, references are taken from the HOLY BIBLE,
NEW INTERNATIONAL VERSION. © 1973, 1978, 1984 International Bible Society.
Used with permission of Zondervan Bible Publishers.

This edition published 1993 by The Standard Publishing Company
8121 Hamilton Avenue, Cincinnati, Ohio 45231
Division of Standex International Corporation
All rights reserved. Printed in U.S.A.
ISBN 0-7847-0084-2

STANDARD
PUBLISHING
Cincinnati, Ohio

1   ☐ **Pray.** ☐ **Read Genesis 2:4-14.** ☐ **Think about what you read using the three keys on the inside front cover.**

Use the code to learn what God did in the beginning.

A	B	D	E	F	G	I	L	M	N	O	P	R	S	T	U
○	⊖	◉	⊗	⊘	▣	⊝	⦶	◼	◎	⊚	⊕	ⓘ	⊙	▲	⊞

He ___ ___ ___ ___ ___ ___ ___ a ___ ___ ___ ___ ___ ___

in the ___ ___ ___ ___, in ___ ___ ___ ___, and there he

___ ___ ___ the ___ ___ ___ he had ___ ___ ___ ___ ___ ___ .

2   ☐ **Pray.** ☐ **Read Genesis 2:15-19.** ☐ **Think about what you read using the three keys on the inside front cover.**

Do the crossword puzzle to find out about God and the man he created.

God put the man in the ____(1 Across) to ____(3 Down) it. God told the ____ (7 Down), "You may eat from any ____(9 Across) except the tree of the knowledge of good and ____(8 Down). When you eat from it, you'll ____(5 Down)." God said, "It's not ____(6 Across) for the man to be ____(2 Down). I'll ____(7 Across) him a helper." God brought ____(4 Down) and ____(11 Across) to the man to ____(10 Across).

3   ☐ **Pray.** ☐ **Read Genesis 2:20-25.** ☐ **Think about what you read using the three keys on the inside front cover.**

To find out what the man said about the woman and what the Bible teaches about marriage, read the darker words first and then the lighter ones.

"**This** For **is** this **now** reason **bone** a **of** man **my** will **bones** leave **and** his **flesh** father **of** and **my** mother **flesh;** and **she** be **shall** united **be** to **called** his '**woman**' wife **for** and **she** they **was** will **taken** become **out** one **of** flesh **man**."

4   ☐ **Pray.** ☐ **Read Genesis 4:1-7.** ☐ **Think about what you read using the three keys on the inside front cover.**

Use the code to find out what God asked Cain.

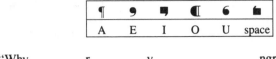

¶	⌐	◄	◖	◔	◕
A	E	I	O	U	space

"Why ___ ___ r ___ ___ y ___ ___ ___ ___ ___ ngry?"

5 □ **Pray.** □ **Read Genesis 4:8-16.** □ **Think about what you read using the three keys on the inside front cover.**
Put the number of each quote in the speech balloon of the person who said it.

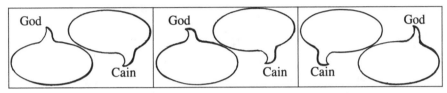

1. "My punishment is too hard."
2. "Where is your brother?"
3. "What have you done? Now you are cursed."
4. "No! I'll put a mark on you."
5. "I don't know. Am I my brother's keeper?"
6. "Whoever finds me will kill me."

▶ □ **Weekend Review**
Recite your memory verse to an adult. In your notebook, list three ways to care for plant life in God's creation (such as plant a seedling tree, recycle paper, water houseplants). Do one of them this week.

WEEK 2 □ Memorize: Genesis 6:8

1 □ **Pray.** □ **Read Genesis 6:1-8.** □ **Think about what you read using the three keys on the inside front cover.**
Circle the correct word in each pair to see what God thought.

God saw how **bad/sad** people's **life/wickedness** had become. He was **glad/sorry** he had **made/seen** mankind. He decided, "I will wipe out **birds/mankind,** that I **hated/created,** from the **face/clouds** of the **heavens/earth.**" But Noah **found/lost** favor in God's **home/eyes.**

2 □ **Pray.** □ **Read Genesis 6:9-16.** □ **Think about what you read using the three keys on the inside front cover.**
Connect the dots to see what God talked to Noah about.

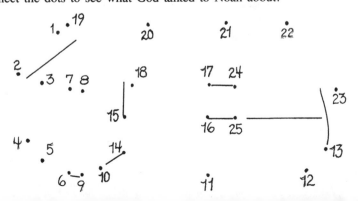

3 □ **Pray.** □ **Read Genesis 6:17-22.** □ **Think about what you read using the three keys on the inside front cover.**

Use the code to find out what Noah did after God told him to build an ark.

Z	Y	X	W	V	U	T	S	R	Q	P	O	N	M	L	K	J	I	H	G	F	E	D	C	B	A
A	B	C	D	E	F	G	H	I	J	K	L	M	N	O	P	Q	R	S	T	U	V	W	X	Y	Z

_____

S V   W R W   V E V I B G S R M T   Q F H G   Z H   T L W

_____

X L N N Z M W V W   S R N

4 □ **Pray.** □ **Read Genesis 7:1-5.** □ **Think about what you read using the three keys on the inside front cover.**

Mark each statement about the flood either *true (T)* or *false (F)*.

_____ The Lord told Noah to go into the ark by himself.

_____ The Lord said Noah was righteous.

_____ Noah was to take two of every kind of clean animal into the ark.

_____ Noah was to take two of every kind of unclean animal into the ark.

_____ Noah was to take three of every kind of bird into the ark.

_____ The animals were saved so Noah's family would have food in the ark.

_____ The Lord said in seven days he would send hail on the earth.

_____ Rain would fall, and all living creatures not in the ark would die.

5 □ **Pray.** □ **Read Genesis 7:6-12.** □ **Think about what you read using the three keys on the inside front cover.**

Fill in the blanks with the correct numbers about Noah and the flood.

2   7   17   40   600

Noah was ____ years old when the flood came. Creatures of all kinds came by ____'s into the ark. ____ days later, the flood came. It was the ____th day of the second month. Rain fell for ____ days and nights.

▶ □ **Weekend Review**

Recite your memory verse to an adult. Choose a project your family can do to help wildlife (such as making a bird feeder). Write what you'll do in your notebook.

1 □ **Pray.** □ **Read Genesis 7:13-16.** □ **Think about what you read using the three keys on the inside front cover.**

Write in the first letters of the animals to see what God shut in the ark with Noah and his family.

____ ____ I ___ S ___ F A ___ L ___ I N ____ ____

O ____ ____ R ___ A ___ U ___ E ____

2 □ **Pray.** □ **Read Genesis 7:17-24.** □ **Think about what you read using the three keys on the inside front cover.**

Search up, down, and diagonally for words from the story of the flood.

flood	mountains
earth	heaven
water	livestock
ark	animals
birds	creatures
Noah	mankind

```
N  D  N  I  K  N  A  M  O  F  F  A
E  C  R  E  A  T  U  R  E  S  L  N
V  A  T  N  M  Z  E  B  K  L  O  I
A  Z  O  S  N  I  A  T  N  U  O  M
E  A  K  O  B  I  R  D  S  Y  D  A
H  E  R  K  C  O  T  S  E  V  I  L
S  W  A  T  E  R  H  Q  P  E  T  S
```

3 □ **Pray.** □ **Read Genesis 8:1-5.** □ **Think about what you read using the three keys on the inside front cover.**

Fill in the broken letters to find out where the ark landed.

ON THE MOUNTAINS OF ARARAT

4 □ **Pray.** □ **Read Genesis 8:6-12.** □ **Think about what you read using the three keys on the inside front cover.**

Number the sentences in the correct order.

____ Noah sent out a raven.

____ The dove returned.

____ The dove did not return.

____ Noah waited seven days and sent out the dove again.

____ After 40 days, Noah opened the window.

____ Noah sent out a dove.

____ After seven days, Noah sent out a dove a third time.

____ The dove brought back an olive branch.

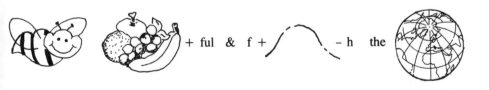

5
☐ **Pray.**   ☐ **Read Genesis 8:13-19.**   ☐ **Think about what you read using the three keys on the inside front cover.**
Use the code to find out what God told Noah to do when the earth was dry.

○	△	✧	●	▲	✳
a	e	i	o	u	space

"C __ m __ __ __ t __ __ f __ th __ __ __ r k __ w
   ●   △   ✳   ●   ▲   '   ✳   ●   ✳   △   ✳   ○   ✳

__ th __ y __ __ r __ f __ m __ ly. __ B r __ n g __ __
✧   ✳   ● ▲   ✳   ○   ✧   ✳   ✧   ✳   ●

__ t __ __ l l __ t h __ __ c r __ __ t __ r __ s __ s
▲   ✳   ○   ✳   △   ✳   △ ○   ▲   △   ✳

__ __ t h __ y __ c __ n __ m __ l t __ ply."
● ✳   △   ✳   ○   ✳   ▲   ✧

▶ ☐ **Weekend Review**
Recite your memory verse to an adult. Choose one way you can help take care of a family pet or neighborhood animal this week. Draw the animal in your notebook.

WEEK 4   ☐ Memorize: Genesis 9:11

1
☐ **Pray.**   ☐ **Read Genesis 8:20-22.**   ☐ **Think about what you read using the three keys on the inside front cover.**
Circle the things God promised would continue as long as the earth endures.

day and night	moon and stars	cold and heat
sun and rain	wind and waves	land and ocean
plants and animals	seedtime and harvest	summer and winter

2
☐ **Pray.**   ☐ **Read Genesis 9:1-7.**   ☐ **Think about what you read using the three keys on the inside front cover.**
Use the sounds of the objects to find out what God said to Noah and his sons.

+ ful & f + /⁀\ - h the

☐ **Pray.**   ☐ **Read Genesis 9:8-17.**   ☐ **Think about what you read using the three keys on the inside front cover.**

Finish the scene to show the sign of God's covenant (agreement) with all living creatures.

☐ **Pray.**   ☐ **Read Genesis 11:1-4.**   ☐ **Think about what you read using the three keys on the inside front cover.**

Use the code to find out what the people planned to build.

A	C	E	H	N	O	R	S	T	V	W	space

_____

_____

☐ **Pray.**   ☐ **Read Genesis 11:5-9.**   ☐ **Think about what you read using the three keys on the inside front cover.**

Check either the *yes* or the *no* box of what happened at the Tower of Babel.

Yes No

☐ ☐ God heard about the tower people were building.

☐ ☐ God decided to confuse the people's language.

☐ ☐ The people could understand different languages.

☐ ☐ God scattered the people throughout the city.

☐ ☐ The people kept on building the tower.

▶ ☐ **Weekend Review**

Recite your memory verse to an adult. Ask someone who speaks another language to teach you some of it. Write the words in your notebook and use them this week.

1 ☐ **Pray.** ☐ **Read Luke 1:26-38.** ☐ **Think about what you read using the three keys on the inside front cover.**

Use the code to find out what the angel said to Mary.

1	2	3	4	5	6	7	8	9	10	11	12	13	14	15	16	17	18	19	20	21	22	23	24	25	26
a	b	c	d	e	f	g	h	i	j	k	l	m	n	o	p	q	r	s	t	u	v	w	x	y	z

___ ___ ___ ___   ___ ___   ___ ___ ___ ___ ___ ___ . ___ ___ ___
 4 15 14 20   2   5   1   6 18   1   9   4   25 15 21

___ ___ ___ ___   ___ ___ ___ ___   ___   ___ ___ ___ .
23   9 12 12   8   1 22   5   1   19 15 14

___ ___ ___ ___   ___ ___ ___   ___ ___ ___ ___ ___ .
 3   1 12 12   8   9 13   10   5 19 21 19

2 ☐ **Pray.** ☐ **Read Luke 1:39-45.** ☐ **Think about what you read using the three keys on the inside front cover.**

To see what Elizabeth said to Mary, cross out all the words beginning with *T*.

therefore tell blessed true are thousand talking you thankful among ten women!

3 ☐ **Pray.** ☐ **Read Luke 1:57-66.** ☐ **Think about what you read using the three keys on the inside front cover.**

To see what Zechariah wrote, add one line to each figure to make letters.

4 ☐ **Pray.** ☐ **Read Luke 2:1-7.** ☐ **Think about what you read using the three keys on the inside front cover.**

Fit the words from the story of Jesus' birth into the word *BETHLEHEM*.

MARY
JOSEPH
BABY
MANGER
TAXES

□ **Pray.** □ **Read Luke 2:8-20.** □ **Think about what you read using the three keys on the inside front cover.**

Use the code to find out what the angel told the shepherds.

☆	●	✳	☆	★
a	e	i	o	u

___ br___ng y_____ g_____d n___ws ___f gr_____t
✳ ✳   ☆ ★ ☆ ☆   ● ☆ ● ☆

j ___y f___r ___ll p_____pl___. T___d___y ___
☆   ☆   ☆   ● ☆ ●   ★ ☆   ☆

S___v_____r h___s b_____n b___rn t___ y_____.
☆ ✳ ☆   ☆   ● ●   ★   ★ ★ ★

H___ ___s Chr___st th___ L___rd. Y_____ w___ll
● ✳   ✳   ● ☆   ★ ★   ✳

f___nd h___m ly___ng ___n ___ m___ng___r.
✳   ✳   ✳   ✳ ☆ ☆ ●

▶ □ **Weekend Review**

Recite your memory verse to an adult. This week, tell someone younger than you the story of Jesus' birth. You may want to use the figures from a manger scene.

WEEK 6   □ Memorize: Matthew 6:20

1 □ **Pray.** □ **Read Matthew 6:1-8.** □ **Think about what you read using the three keys on the inside front cover.**

Hold your book up to a mirror to see how Jesus said to do a good deed.

ꓘƎƎꟼ IꓕA 丨Ƨ Ɔ Ǝ ꓤ ƆꓤƎꓕ

2 □ **Pray.** □ **Read Matthew 6:9-15.** □ **Think about what you read using the three keys on the inside front cover.**

Match the phrases from the prayer Jesus taught his disciples.

Give us today	as we forgive people who sin against us.
Our Father in heaven	but save us from the evil one.
May your kingdom come and your will be done	may your name be kept holy.
Don't lead us into temptation	our daily food.
Forgive us our sins	on earth as it is in heaven.

3

☐ Pray. ☐ Read Matthew 6:16-18. ☐ Think about what you read using the three keys on the inside front cover.

Use the code to see what will happen if you fast (give up eating to pray and worship) without making a show of it.

▶▶	→	⇥	→	➡	▸	→	↔	➡	⇉	▬	➡	⇨	⇶	⇀	⇚	←
a	c	d	e	f	h	i	l	n	o	r	s	t	u	w	y	space

' '
_____

⇚ ⇉ ⇶ ▬ ← → ⇉ ⇨ ▸ → ▬ ← ⇀ ▸ ⇉ ← ➡ → → → ➡ ← ⇀ ▸ ⇉ ⇨ ←

_____

→ ➡ ← ⇥ ⇉ ➡ → ← → ➡ ← ➡ → → ▬ → ⇨ ← ⇀ → → ↔ ↔ ←

_____ ' '

▬ → ⇀ ⇉ ▬ ⇥ ← ⇚ ⇉ ⇶

4

☐ Pray. ☐ Read Matthew 6:19-24. ☐ Think about what you read using the three keys on the inside front cover.

Search across, down, and diagonally for words that Jesus talked about.

store	lamp											
treasures	light	E	Y	D	O	B	S	E	R	V	E	T	A	H	T
earth	darkness	A	Y	E	N	O	M	T	L	I	G	H	T	Z	R
moth	masters	R	S	E	R	U	S	A	E	R	T	I	N	T	A
rust	love	T	T	V	Q	U	O	W	G	O	D	E	P	R	E
thieves	hate	H	O	O	R	P	L	S	M	N	E	V	A	E	H
heaven	serve	U	R	L	A	M	P	M	A	S	T	E	R	S	E
heart	God	B	E	N	D	A	R	K	N	E	S	S	E	T	N
eye	Money														
body															

5

☐ Pray. ☐ Read Matthew 6:25-34. ☐ Think about what you read using the three keys on the inside front cover.

Draw a "Do" or "Don't" sign by each phrase to show what Jesus wants us to do.

(Do)   (Don't)

look at the birds
worry about clothes

look at the field lilies

worry about what you'll eat or drink
seek first God's kingdom and his
   righteousness
worry about tomorrow

▶ ☐ Weekend Review

Recite your memory verse to an adult. Choose a family member or friend as a secret pal this week. Choose three kind things to do secretly for your pal. List them in your notebook, and check them off after you've done them.

1 ☐ **Pray.** ☐ **Read John 4:1-10.** ☐ **Think about what you read using the three keys on the inside front cover.**

Connect the dashes to see what Jesus said he would give the Samaritan woman.

2 ☐ **Pray.** ☐ **Read John 4:11-26.** ☐ **Think about what you read using the three keys on the inside front cover.**

Next to the Samaritan woman's statements, put the number of the reply Jesus made.

Samaritan woman

____ "You have nothing to draw water with."

"Sir, give me this water."

____ "But Jews worship in Jerusalem while Samaritans don't."

____ "I know the Messiah is coming."

"I don't have a husband."

Jesus

4. "Those who drink my water will never get thirsty again."

1. "True. You've had five husbands."

3. "True worshipers will worship God in spirit and truth."

5. "Go, bring your husband."

2. "I am he."

3 ☐ **Pray.** ☐ **Read John 4:27-38.** ☐ **Think about what you read using the three keys on the inside front cover.**

Read every third word to see what Jesus said when his disciples offered him food.

"Your Their My drink wish food was can is of for to be say do a an the words people will on to of them those him when where who see want sent you them me."

4 ☐ **Pray.** ☐ **Read John 4:39-42.** ☐ **Think about what you read using the three keys on the inside front cover.**

Use the code to see what the townspeople told the Samaritan woman about Jesus.

a	e	i	o	u	space
◤	◥	◣	◢	◫	◼

W◤ ◫n◣ ◫l◣ng◥ r◫b◤l◣ ◥v◤ ◫j◫ st◫b◤

c◤ ◫s◤ ◥ ◣f◫wh◤t◫y◣ ◫ ◫s◤ ◣d◫ ; w◤

◫h◤v◥ ◫h◤ ◤rd◫f◣r◫ ◫ ◫rs◤lv◥s◫ ◤

nd◫w◤ ◫kn◣w◫h◥ ◫r◥ ◤lly◫ ◣s◫th◥ ◫

S◤v◣ ◣r◫ ◣f◫th◥ ◫w◣rld.

5 ☐ **Pray.** ☐ **Read John 4:43-54.** ☐ **Think about what you read using the three keys on the inside front cover.**

To see what happened in Cana, cross out the wrong word in each pair.

A royal **official/servant** asked Jesus, "Please come **teach/heal** my son." Jesus said, "You may **believe/go.** Your son will **walk/live.**" The man believed Jesus and **left/cried.** While he was still on the **run/way,** his **servants/wife** met him with the **plea/news** that his son was **dead/living.** He got **better/worse** at the exact **place/time** Jesus had said, "Your son will **walk/live.**"

▶ ☐ **Weekend Review**

Recite your memory verse to an adult. In your notebook, make a coded message of what you learned about Jesus this week. Give it to a friend to figure out. Tell your friend what you learned about Jesus this week.

WEEK 8 ☐ Memorize: John 10:11

1 ☐ **Pray.** **Read John 10:1-6.** ☐ **Think about what you read using the three keys on the inside front cover.**

Follow the words through the maze to see what Jesus said about the good shepherd.

```
Start→  H N A M E P B Y N A R O W L L O W H I M Y T O E I C E  ←Finish
        E C Y D O E I N E M R A H O M E S E M A N N E W O N E
        R A N D G E H S M E A N Y F P E D E B T O E Y E V S E
        S L L S F O N N O S O D A T E E P C R E T H K E Y I T
        B M A H I S O W T E N H I S S H E A U S E T N O W H O
```

2 ☐ **Pray.** ☐ **Read John 10:7-13.** ☐ **Think about what you read using the three keys on the inside front cover.**

Use the code to find out what Jesus said was the reason he came to earth.

A	E	F	H	I	L	M	O	T	U	V	Y

3 ☐ **Pray.** ☐ **Read John 10:14-21.** ☐ **Think about what you read using the three keys on the inside front cover.**

Circle every other word to see what Jesus the Good Shepherd said he does.

I You lay put down up my their life paths for beside the your sheep followers.

4 ☐ **Pray.** ☐ **Read John 10:22-30.** ☐ **Think about what you read using the three keys on the inside front cover.**

Unscramble the words to find out what Jesus replied when asked to say plainly if he was the Christ.

"I told you but you don't **vibelee** _____. The **srcamile** _____

I do speak for me. You don't believe because you're not my **ephes** _____. They

listen to my **eivco** _____. I give them **ratleen feil** _____.

They shall never **hispre** _____. No one can **tcansh** _____ them

out of my Father's hand."

5 ☐ **Pray.** ☐ **Read John 10:31-42.** ☐ **Think about what you read using the three keys on the inside front cover.**

Match the statements and quotes to the correct people.

People across the Jordan River

"All that John the Baptist said about him is true."

"Don't believe me unless I do what my Father does."

"We're going to stone you because you claim to be God."

Did many miracles

Tried to capture Jesus

Believed in Jesus

Escaped

"The Father is in me, and I am in the Father."

Jewish leaders in Jerusalem

Jesus

▶ ☐ **Weekend Review**

Recite your memory verse to an adult. In your notebook, list three ways you can follow Jesus this week. Check them off as you do them.

1 ☐ **Pray.** ☐ **Read Exodus 1:1-10.** ☐ **Think about what you read using the three keys on the inside front cover.**

Use the sounds of the objects and symbols to see what Pharaoh, the king of Egypt, told his people about the Israelites.

Th + 🧑‍🦱 **R 2** 👨👨👨 **+E 4** 🚌 -b

2 ☐ **Pray.** ☐ **Read Exodus 1:11-22.** ☐ **Think about what you read using the three keys on the inside front cover.**

Use the code to find out the order Pharaoh gave about the Israelites.

A	B	C	D	E	F	G	H	I	J	K	L	M	N	O	P	Q	R	S	T	U	V	W	X	Y	Z	space
26	25	24	23	22	21	20	19	18	17	16	15	14	13	12	11	10	9	8	7	6	5	4	3	2	1	0

_____

7 19 9 12 4 0 22 5 22 9 2 0 25 12 2 0 25 26 25 2 0 18 13 7 12 0

_____

7 19 22 0 13 18 15 22 0 9 18 5 22 9 0 25 6 7 0 15 22 7 0 7 19 22 0

_____

20 18 9 15 8 0 15 18 5 22

3 ☐ **Pray.** ☐ **Read Exodus 2:1-10.** ☐ **Think about what you read using the three keys on the inside front cover.**

Fill in the blanks. The circled letters spell the name that means "draw out."

A Levite ___ ___ (○) ___ ___ gave birth to a son.

The baby's ___ (○) ___ ___ ___ ___ hid him in a basket in the river.

The baby's ___ ___ (○) ___ ___ ___ watched him.

The king's ___ ___ ___ ___ ___ ___ (○) ___ found the baby in the reeds.

She paid the baby's mother to ___ ___ ___ (○) ___ him for her.

4 ☐ **Pray.** ☐ **Read Exodus 2:11-17.** ☐ **Think about what you read using the three keys on the inside front cover.**

Use the code to see what Moses did after Pharaoh found out he killed an Egyptian.

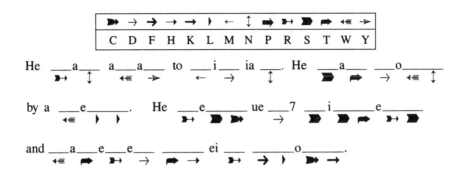

▶	→	→	→	→	↘	←	↕	➡	▶	⏩	➡	◀	⇀
C	D	F	H	K	L	M	N	P	R	S	T	W	Y

He __a__ a__a__ to __i__ ia __. He __a__ __o_____

by a __e_____. He __e_____ ue __7 __i_____e_____

and ___a__e__e__ _____ ei __ _____o_____.

---

5 ☐ **Pray.** ☐ **Read Exodus 2:18-25.** ☐ **Think about what you read using the three keys on the inside front cover.**

Cross out what God did **not** do when the Israelites groaned and cried out to him.

he heard them   he left them   he looked on them   he carried them

he remembered his covenant   he punished them   he was concerned about them

---

▶ ☐ **Weekend Review**

Recite your memory verse to an adult. In a baby book, find out what each family member's name means. Make a place mat or name plaque for each using the meaning.

WEEK 10 ☐ **Memorize: Exodus 3:14**

1 ☐ **Pray.** ☐ **Read Exodus 3:1-10.** ☐ **Think about what you read using the three keys on the inside front cover.**

Follow the flames from the bush to the letters to see what God said he would do. Don't cross lines to get to the letters.

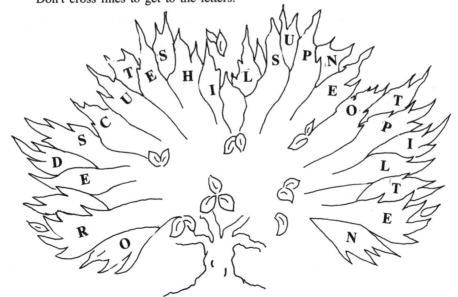

2 ☐ **Pray.** ☐ **Read Exodus 3:11-22.** ☐ **Think about what you read using the three keys on the inside front cover.**

Put Moses' questions and God's answers in the correct speech balloons.

"I'll be with you."   "What should I say when they ask your name?"

"Who am I to go to Pharaoh?"   "Tell them I AM has sent you."

3 ☐ **Pray.** ☐ **Read Exodus 4:18-23, 27-31.** ☐ **Think about what you read using the three keys on the inside front cover.**

Use the code to see what the Israelites did after Moses spoke and performed signs.

a	e	i	o	u
□	△	○	☆	◆

Th△y b△l○△v△d, b☆w△d d☆wn, □nd w☆rsh○p△d G☆d.

4 ☐ **Pray.** ☐ **Read Exodus 5:1-9.** ☐ **Think about what you read using the three keys on the inside front cover.**

Cross out the !s and &s to find out what Pharaoh said about God's command.

&Wh!!oist!&he&!Lo!!rdt!!!hat&Is&!&houl!!do!be&&y!hi!!ma&!ndl!!et&&!Is!ra!&!elgo?!

5 ☐ **Pray.** ☐ **Read Exodus 5:10-21.** ☐ **Think about what you read using the three keys on the inside front cover.**

Read across the wall, skipping the cracked bricks, to see what Pharaoh said to the Israelites when they complained about having to make bricks without straw.

They	You	are	right	lazy	That's	why	you	need	want	to	work
go	and	worship	me	God	You	will	buy	get	no	help	straw
but	you	must	build	make	the	way	same	tower	number	of	bricks

▶ ☐ **Weekend Review**

Recite your memory verse to an adult. In your notebook, list two ways you could help poor or homeless people in your community, such as by giving to a food pantry. Do one of those things this week.

1 ☐ **Pray.** ☐ **Read Exodus 7:1-7.** ☐ **Think about what you read using the three keys on the inside front cover.**

Use the code to see what God said to Moses about getting his people out of Egypt.

①	❶	②	❷	③	❸	④	❹	⑤	❺	⑥	❻	⑦	❼	⑧	❽	⑨	❾	⑩	⓾
a	c	d	e	f	g	h	i	l	m	n	o	p	r	s	t	u	y	z	space

I will _____
② ❻ ⓾ ❺ ① ⑥ ❾ ⓾ ❺ ❹ ❼ ① ❶ ⑤ ❷ ⑧ ⓾ ❹ ⑥ ⓾ ❷ ❸ ❾ ⑦ ⑧

I will _____
⑤ ❷ ① ② ⓾ ❺ ❾ ⓾ ⑦ ❷ ⑥ ⑦ ⑤ ❷ ⓾ ⑥ ⑨ ⑧

The Egyptians will _____
③ ❹ ⑥ ② ⓾ ⑥ ⑨ ⑧ ⓾ ⑧ ④ ① ⑧ ⓾ ❹ ⓾ ① ❺ ⓾

_____
⑧ ④ ❷ ⓾ ⑤ ⑥ ❼ ②

2 ☐ **Pray.** ☐ **Read Exodus 10:1-11.** ☐ **Think about what you read using the three keys on the inside front cover.**

Trace the Zs to see what God sent after the plague of hail.

```
Z B B B B B Z Z Z Z B B Z Z Z Z B B Z B B Z H H Z Z Z Z H H Z Z Z Z Z H H Z Z Z Z
Z B B B E E Z E E Z P P Z P P B B B Z B E Z E E Z E P P P P P E Z E E E E Z E E E
Z B B B B E Z E P Z P P Z P P P P E Z E E Z B B Z Z Z Z B B B B Z B E E P Z Z Z Z
Z B B B B B Z E P Z P P Z P P P B B Z B B Z B E E P P Z P P P B Z B B E E E E E Z
Z Z Z Z E E Z Z Z Z P P Z Z Z Z B B Z Z Z Z E E Z Z Z Z E E E B Z B B B E Z Z Z Z
```

3 ☐ **Pray.** ☐ **Read Exodus 10:12-20.** ☐ **Think about what you read using the three keys on the inside front cover.**

Mark the statements either *True* or *False*.

_____ Moses raised his staff over the Israelites.

_____ God made an east wind blow and bring locusts to Egypt.

_____ The locusts ate most of the plants left by the hail.

_____ Pharaoh said, "I've sinned. Forgive me. Ask God to take away the plague."

_____ God changed the wind to a north wind that blew the locusts into the Red Sea.

_____ Then Pharaoh let the Israelites go to worship God.

4 ☐ **Pray.** ☐ **Read Exodus 11:1-10.** ☐ **Think about what you read using the three keys on the inside front cover.**

To find out what the last plague sent on Egypt was, read the phrases in the same order as the pattern in the box.

◦•	○	▶	✓	☆	●

▶in Egypt ☆in Israel ○firstborn sons ◦•all the ●will die ✓but not

5 ☐ **Pray.** ☐ **Read Exodus 12:31-42.** ☐ **Think about what you read using the three keys on the inside front cover.**

Search for words from the story of the night that the Israelites left Egypt.

king	herds	E	A	T	R	O	U	G	H	S	O	S	K	C	O	L	F	Y
Moses	bless	S	G	N	I	K	I	D	A	Y	R	R	U	H	W	I	S	E
Aaron	dough	I	S	R	A	E	L	I	T	E	S	E	E	M	O	S	E	S
leave	yeast	L	O	A	D	O	U	G	H	B	L	E	S	S	R	E	D	O
worship	troughs	V	E	T	G	R	O	W	E	S	U	P	E	A	S	E	N	D
Israelites	silver	E	M	A	A	R	O	N	R	E	C	L	O	T	H	I	N	G
Egyptians	gold	R	O	B	V	A	M	E	D	P	W	M	S	E	I	S	O	R
hurry	clothing	A	T	S	A	E	Y	E	S	S	N	A	I	T	P	Y	G	E
flocks	people																	

▶ ☐ **Weekend Review**

Recite your memory verse to an adult. From your church, get a prayer card from a missionary family whose main job is telling people about God. Pray for them this week.

WEEK 12 ☐ Memorize: Exodus 14:14

1 ☐ **Pray.** ☐ **Read Exodus 13:17-14:4.** ☐ **Think about what you read using the three keys on the inside front cover.**

Follow the arrows to find out how God led the Israelites.

Start ➡

2 ☐ **Pray.** ☐ **Read Exodus 14:5-18.** ☐ **Think about what you read using the three keys on the inside front cover.**

Use the code to find out what Moses told the Israelites when Pharoah chased them.

A	B	C	D	E	F	G	H	I	J	K	L	M	N	O	P	Q	R	S	T	U	V	W	X	Y	Z
c	d	e	f	g	h	i	j	k	l	m	n	o	p	q	r	s	t	u	v	w	x	y	z	a	b

BML'R ZC YDPYGB. QRYLB QRGJJ YLB WMS'JJ QCC EMB

QYTC WMS RMBYW. WMS'JJ LCTCP QCC RFCQC CEWNRGYLQ

YEYGL. EMB UGJJ DGEFR DMP WMS.

3

☐ **Pray.** ☐ **Read Exodus 14:19-31.** ☐ **Think about what you read using the three keys on the inside front cover.**

Number the events of the Red Sea crossing in the correct order.

____ The Egyptian army followed the Israelites through the sea.

____ The Israelites feared and trusted God.

____ Moses held his hand over the sea.

____ The whole Egyptian army that followed the Israelites drowned.

____ The Israelites walked across the sea through walls of water.

____ God ruined the wheels of the Egyptian chariots.

____ God sent a strong east wind that blew all night and made the sea dry.

____ The sea came back again after God told Moses to hold out his hand.

4

☐ **Pray.** ☐ **Read Exodus 15:22-27.** ☐ **Think about what you read using the three keys on the inside front cover.**

Use the code to find out what happened when Moses threw wood into water at Marah.

✓	{	#	|	¶	†	‡	§
b	d	h	m	r	s	t	w

I __ __ a __ e __ __ e __ i __ __ e __
    ‡ | {   ‡ #   ✓ ‡ ‡   ¶

__ a __ e __ __ __ e e __ .
 §   ‡   ¶   † §   ‡

5

☐ **Pray.** ☐ **Read Exodus 16:1-16.** ☐ **Think about what you read using the three keys on the inside front cover.**

Do the math problems first, and then write in the correct letters to see what God gave the Israelites in the desert.

1	2	3	4	5	6	7	8	9	10	11	12	13	14
a	b	c	d	e	f	g	m	n	o	p	r	s	t

$$\begin{array}{r} 13 \\ -5 \\ \hline \end{array} \quad \begin{array}{r} 15 \\ -10 \\ \hline \end{array} \quad \begin{array}{r} 23 \\ -22 \\ \hline \end{array} \quad \begin{array}{r} 5 \\ +9 \\ \hline \end{array}$$

☐ ☐ ☐ ☐ = _____ each evening

$$\begin{array}{r} 16 \\ -14 \\ \hline \end{array} \quad \begin{array}{r} 4 \\ +8 \\ \hline \end{array} \quad \begin{array}{r} 11 \\ -6 \\ \hline \end{array} \quad \begin{array}{r} 17 \\ -16 \\ \hline \end{array} \quad \begin{array}{r} 25 \\ -21 \\ \hline \end{array}$$

☐ ☐ ☐ ☐ ☐ = _____ each morning

▶ ☐ **Weekend Review**

Recite your memory verse to an adult. In your notebook, write a prayer thanking God for the food, care, and help he gives you. Read it at a family meal this week.

1 ☐ **Pray.** ☐ **Read Exodus 19:1-8.** ☐ **Think about what you read using the three keys on the inside front cover.**
Do the crossword puzzle to find out what God told Moses to tell the Israelites.

You've seen what I did to ____ (*7 Down*). I brought you to ____ (*6 Down*) on ____ (*7 Across*) wings. If you ____ (*8 Across*) me, you'll be my treasured ____ (*3 Across*) out of all the ____ (*5 Down*). Although the whole ____ (*4 Down*) is mine, you'll be my special ____ (*2 Down*) of priests and a ____ (*1 Down*) nation.

2 ☐ **Pray.** ☐ **Read Exodus 19:9-15.** ☐ **Think about what you read using the three keys on the inside front cover.**
Use the code to find out what God said to the Israelites about Mount Sinai.

①	②	③	④	⑤	⑥	⑦	⑧	⑨	⑩	Ⓒ
a	c	d	e	h	i	m	n	o	t	u

③ ⑨ ⑧ ' ⑩   ⑩ ⑨ Ⓒ ② ⑤   ⑩ ⑤ ④   ⑦ ⑨ Ⓒ ⑧ ⑩ ① ⑥ ⑧

3 ☐ **Pray.** ☐ **Read Exodus 19:16-25.** ☐ **Think about what you read using the three keys on the inside front cover.**
Finish the scene showing Mount Sinai when God came there to speak to Moses.

4 □ **Pray.** □ **Read Exodus 20:1-11.** □ **Think about what you read using the three keys on the inside front cover.**
Separate the letters into words to see what God said on Mount Sinai.

Iamt he Lo rdy our Go dwh obro ughty ouou tofE gyptw here yo uwe res laves.

5 □ **Pray.** □ **Read Exodus 20:12-21.** □ **Think about what you read using the three keys on the inside front cover.**
Circle the things God commanded.

honor your enemies   don't murder   don't be lazy   don't steal

don't lie   don't argue   honor your father and mother   don't envy

▶ □ **Weekend Review**
Recite your memory verse to an adult. In your notebook, list three ways you can honor your parents. Choose one to especially practice doing this week.

WEEK 14 □ Memorize: Luke 8:1

1 □ **Pray.** □ **Read Luke 8:1-3.** □ **Think about what you read using the three keys on the inside front cover.**
Use the code to find out what the women who traveled with Jesus did.

$	%	¢	#	@	✔
A	E	I	O	U	Y

T h % ✔   @ s % d   t h % ¢ r   # w n   m # n % ✔   t #   h % l p

J % s @ s $ n d   t h %   d ¢ s c ¢ p l % s.

2 □ **Pray.** □ **Read Luke 8:4-15.** □ **Think about what you read using the three keys on the inside front cover.**
To see what Jesus said the seed in his story was, write the words from the correct puzzle pieces in the puzzle frame.

3 □ **Pray.** □ **Read Luke 8:16-18.** □ **Think about what you read using the three keys on the inside front cover.**

Unscramble the words to see what Jesus told the disciples.

No one **thigls** _____ a **plam** _____ and then **dishe** _____ it. Instead,

he puts it on a **dants** _____ so others who **moec** _____ can have **hitgl**

_____. **givethreyn** _____ that is **dinehd** _____ will

be shown. Every **treecs** _____ will be made **wonnk** _____. Be **facelur**

_____ how you **lensit** _____.

4 □ **Pray.** □ **Read Luke 10:25-37.** □ **Think about what you read using the three keys on the inside front cover.**

Search for words from the story Jesus told about the good Samaritan.

teacher	Samaritan	R	O	B	H	G	I	E	N	A	M	E	R	C	Y	O	N
law	pity	O	I	A	L	L	R	E	P	E	E	K	N	N	I	T	E
Jesus	bandaged	A	L	N	W	M	E	L	A	S	U	R	E	J	U	G	S
man	wounds	D	R	D	O	N	K	E	Y	E	S	J	E	S	U	S	T
oil	Jerusalem	E	E	A	U	P	O	N	A	T	I	R	A	M	A	S	O
Jericho	wine	S	H	G	N	A	P	S	E	T	I	V	E	L	A	W	F
road	donkey	S	C	E	D	O	C	N	I	C	E	P	R	I	E	S	T
robbers	inn	A	A	D	S	N	A	I	H	A	D	E	N	T	N	O	A
clothes	care	P	E	A	R	E	R	O	B	B	E	R	S	A	T	N	E
beat	coins	S	T	W	I	N	E	C	S	E	H	T	O	L	C	A	B
priest	innkeeper																
Levite	neighbor																
passed	mercy																

5 □ **Pray.** □ **Read Luke 10:38-42.** □ **Think about what you read using the three keys on the inside front cover.**

To see what Martha asked Jesus, read every other word from left to right. To see what Jesus replied, read the words in capital letters from right to left.

Lord HER Mary FROM has AWAY left TAKEN me BE to WON'T do IT all

AND the THING work RIGHT Tell THE her CHOSEN to HAS help MARY me

▶ □ **Weekend Review**

Recite your memory verse to an adult. Draw or find pictures to illustrate one of Jesus' stories from this week's Bible readings. Use the pictures to tell the story to a younger child.

1 ☐ **Pray.** ☐ **Read Mark 10:13-16.** ☐ **Think about what you read using the three keys on the inside front cover.**

Use the code to find out what Jesus said about children.

😐	😊	😑	🙂	😮	◯
a	e	i	o	y	space

L🙂t ◯ th😊◯ ch😑 ldr😊n ◯ c🙂 m😊◯ t🙂 ◯ m

😊◯ G😑 d's ◯ k🙂 ngd😑 m ◯ b😊l😑 ngs ◯ t😑 ◯

th😑 s😑◯ wh😑◯😐 r😑◯ l😐 k😑◯ ch😑 ldr😊n.

2 ☐ **Pray.** ☐ **Read Mark 10:17-27.** ☐ **Think about what you read using the three keys on the inside front cover.**

Mark the statements *T* for *True* or *F* for *False*.

_____ A man asked Jesus how he could get rich.

_____ The man said, "I've obeyed them all since I was a boy."

_____ Jesus looked at the man and loved him.

_____ Jesus told the man to go home and pray.

_____ The man was sad to hear what Jesus said because he was rich.

_____ Jesus said, "It's impossible for the rich to enter God's kingdom."

_____ The disciples wondered how anyone could be saved.

_____ Jesus said, "It's impossible for human beings, but God can do all things."

3 ☐ **Pray.** ☐ **Read Mark 10:28-34.** ☐ **Think about what you read using the three keys on the inside front cover.**

Use the code to see what Jesus told his disciples when he talked with them alone.

1	2	3	4	5	6	7	8	9	10	11	12	13	14	15	16	17	18	19	20	21	22	23	24	25	26
a	b	c	d	e	f	g	h	i	j	k	l	m	n	o	p	q	r	s	t	u	v	w	x	y	z

9 14   10 5 18 21 19 1 12 5 13   9   23 9 12 12   2 5

11 9 12 12 5 4   2 21 20   15 14   20 8 5   20 8 9 18 4   4 1 25

9   12 12   3 15 13 5   2 1 3 11   20 15   12 9 6 5

4 ☐ **Pray** ☐ **Read Mark 10:35-45.** ☐ **Think about what you read using the three keys on the inside front cover.**
Cross out the *W*s to find out what Jesus said about why he came to earth.

WTwhWewSownwofwMawnwcawmewtowswewrvwew,wnowtwtwowbewswervewdw,

wandwtowgiwvewhwiswlwifewtowswawvewmwanwywwpwewowpwlwew.

5 ☐ **Pray.** ☐ **Read Mark 10:46-52.** ☐ **Think about what you read using the three keys on the inside front cover.**
Fill in the speech balloons with what Bartimaeus, the people, and Jesus said.

Bartimaeus
People | Jesus | People | Jesus | Bartimaeus | Jesus | Bartimaeus

"Be quiet!" "I want to see again." "Tell him to come here." "I can see!"
"Jesus, Son of David, help me!" "He's calling you." "What do you want me to do?"
"Your faith has healed you."

▶ ☐ **Weekend Review**
Recite your memory verse to an adult. In your notebook, list three ways you can help handicapped people in your church, school, or neighborhood, such as by running errands, eating lunch with them, or reading to them. Do one this week.

WEEK 16 ☐ **Memorize: Matthew 22:37**

1 ☐ **Pray.** ☐ **Read Matthew 22:1-14.** ☐ **Think about what you read using the three keys on the inside front cover.**
To see what Jesus said the kingdom of heaven is like, write the first letters of the objects.

____ ____ ____ ____ ____ ____ ____ ____ ____

____ ____ ____ ____ ____

2 ☐ **Pray.** ☐ **Read Matthew 22:15-22.** ☐ **Think about what you read using the three keys on the inside front cover.**
To find out Jesus' answer to a tricky question, first read the small coins in order and then read the large coins in order.

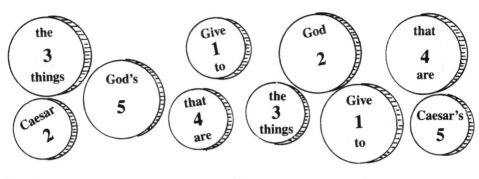

3 □ **Pray.** □ **Read Matthew 22:23-33.** □ **Think about what you read using the three keys on the inside front cover.**

Use the code to find out why Jesus pointed out that God says "I *am* (not I *was*) the God of Abraham, Isaac, and Jacob."

1	2	3	4	5	6	7	8	9	10	11	12	13	14
A	D	E	F	G	H	I	L	N	O	S	T	V	space

_____,

5 10 2 14 7 11 14 12 6 3 14 5 10 2 14 10 4 14 12 6 3 14 8 7 13 7 9 5

_____.

14 9 10 12 14 10 4 14 12 6 3 14 2 3 1 2

4 □ **Pray.** □ **Read Matthew 22:34-40.** □ **Think about what you read using the three keys on the inside front cover.**

To see what Jesus said the greatest commandments are, shade in the boxes marked with squares and then read the other boxes.

○	□	□	○	○	□	○	□	○	○	□	○	□
Love	each	other	God	with	out	all	their	your	heart	body	soul	or

○	○	○	○	□	□	○	□	○	□	○	□	○
and	mind	and	love	treat	the	your	friend	neigh-bor	by	as	well	your-self

5 □ **Pray.** □ **Read Matthew 22:41-46.** □ **Think about what you read using the three keys on the inside front cover.**

To find out what happened when Jesus asked the Pharisees a question, separate the letters into words.

NoonecouldanswerJesus'questionandnoonedaredtoaskJesusanymorequestionsafterthat.

▶ □ **Weekend Review**

Recite your memory verse to an adult. In your notebook, list three ways you could show your love to a family member this week. Check them off as you do them.

1 □ **Pray.** □ **Read Luke 19:1-10.** □ **Think about what you read using the three keys on the inside front cover.**

Follow the line through the words to read what Jesus said to Zacchaeus.

of	God	Man	to	help	and	of	see	people
to	Son	tell	the	to	all	some	lost	found
for	home	came	seek	find	way	after	save

2 □ **Pray.** □ **Read Luke 19:11-19.** □ **Think about what you read using the three keys on the inside front cover.**

Use the code to find out what the first two servants did and got.

+	−	±	÷	×	=
A	E	I	O	W	Y

T h − =   − + r n − d   m ÷ r − $ × ± t h   t h − $ t h − =

× − r −   g ± v − n, & t h −   k ± n g   r − × + r d − d   t h − m.

3 □ **Pray.** □ **Read Luke 19:20-27.** □ **Think about what you read using the three keys on the inside front cover.**

Shade in the spaces marked with dots to see what the third servant did with the money the king gave him.

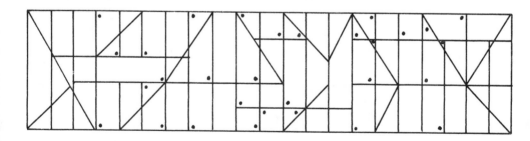

4 □ **Pray.** □ **Read Luke 19:28-38.** □ **Think about what you read using the three keys on the inside front cover.**

Do the puzzle by fitting in words from Jesus' entering Jerusalem as king.

Jesus cloaks
untie road
disciples praise
colt king
ridden name
Jerusalem

5 ☐ **Pray.** ☐ **Read Luke 19:39-48.** ☐ **Think about what you read using the three keys on the inside front cover.**
Cross out words beginning with *M* to find out something Jesus did in Jerusalem.

Men He made more threw mind maybe out the many people who may were marking selling manmade mercy things in midday meal the middle market temple.

▶ ☐ **Weekend Review**
Recite your memory verse to an adult. In your notebook, list three abilities God has given you. This week, talk with an adult about how you can use them to serve God. Record your ideas in your notebook.

WEEK 18 ☐ Memorize: John 15:5

1 ☐ **Pray.** ☐ **Read John 15:1-8.** ☐ **Think about what you read using the three keys on the inside front cover.**
Draw a line from the words in capital letters to what Jesus said they were.

Fire	JESUS	people
glory	FATHER	what pleases God
vine	BRANCHES	food
gardener	FRUIT	truth

2 ☐ **Pray.** ☐ **Read John 15:9-17.** ☐ **Think about what you read using the three keys on the inside front cover.**
Use the code to find out the command Jesus gave his followers.

a	c	d	e	h	l	o	r	s	t	v	space

I _____ you.

3 ☐ **Pray.** ☐ **Read John 15:18-16:4.** ☐ **Think about what you read using the three keys on the inside front cover.**
Skip every other word to see what Jesus told his followers.

The people world love hates me you when because we I've got chosen them you all out for of us it. See Remember, our the home world asked hated you me last first.

4 ☐ **Pray.** ☐ **Read John 16:5-16.** ☐ **Think about what you read using the three keys on the inside front cover.**
Circle the correct word in each pair to see what Jesus said about the Holy Spirit (who is also called the Counselor, the Comforter, and the Helper).

He will prove to **Christians/people** the truth about **sin/Satan**, righteousness, and **salvation/judgment**. He will lead believers into all **happiness/truth**. He will not speak his own **words/pride**. He will **speak/see** only what he hears. He will tell you **who/what** is to come. He will bring glory to **himself/Jesus**.

5 ☐ **Pray.** ☐ **Read John 16:17-33.** ☐ **Think about what you read using the three keys on the inside front cover.**
Use the code to find out what Jesus told his disciples would happen.

A	B	D	E	F	H	K	L	O	R	T	U	V	W
○	⊖	●	≋	▣	⊛	⊖	⦶	■	◎	⬮	⊕	⦶	⊙

You'_ _ _ _ _ _ _ _ _ _ _ _ _ _ in _ _ _

_ _ _ _ _ . _ _ _ _ _ _ _ _ _ _ _ _ !

I _ _ _ _ _ _ _ _ _ _ _ _ _ _ _

_ _ _ _ _ !

▶ ☐ **Weekend Review**
Recite your memory verse to an adult. Make your own coded message about what you learned about Jesus this week. Give it to a friend or family member to solve. Talk to that person about how you will use what you learned.

1 ☐ **Pray.** ☐ **Read Judges 4:1-3.** ☐ **Think about what you read using the three keys on the inside front cover.**

Use the code to find out what the Israelites did after they were treated cruelly.

❶	❷	❸	❹	❺	❻	❼	❽	❾	❿
C	D	E	G	H	I	L	O	P	R

‾‾ ‾‾ ‾‾ ‾‾ ‾‾   to   ‾‾ ‾‾ ‾‾   for   ‾‾ ‾‾ ‾‾ ‾‾
❶ ❿ ❻ ❸ ❷   ❹ ❽ ❷   ❺ ❸ ❼ ❾

2 ☐ **Pray.** ☐ **Read Judges 4:4-10.** ☐ **Think about what you read using the three keys on the inside front cover.**

Find words from the story of how Deborah told Barak to lead the Israelite army.

```
S  H  O  W  S  R  O  B  A  T  T  N  U  O  M  E  T  C
P  A  N  N  E  T  S  I  S  E  R  A  P  N  O  M  O  H
U  R  S  S  E  T  E  H  P  O  R  P  E  E  P  U  E  A
R  O  P  E  N  M  E  A  N  S  A  H  B  A  R  A  K  R
U  B  O  G  N  I  D  A  E  L  O  T  O  T  A  Z  E  I
T  E  O  N  E  T  W  O  M  A  N  A  B  A  W  A  Y  O
O  D  R  I  W  I  A  Z  E  B  U  L  U  N  S  E  A  T
N  O  H  S  I  K  R  E  V  I  R  I  S  R  A  E  L  S
```

Deborah	Naphtali	prophetess	Zebulun
leading	Mount Tabor	Israel	Sisera
court	chariots	palm	River Kishon
Barak	men	God	woman

3 ☐ **Pray.** ☐ **Read Judges 4:11-16.** ☐ **Think about what you read using the three keys on the inside front cover.**

Use the code to see what Deborah told Barak, the commander of Israel's army.

a (square)	e (triangle)	i (circle)	o (star)	u (four-point star)

G☆! T☆d□y G☆d w○ll h△lp
y☆✦ d△f△□t s○s△r□ □nd
h○s □rmy!

4 ☐ **Pray.** ☐ **Read Judges 4:17-21.** ☐ **Think about what you read using the three keys on the inside front cover.**

Fill in the letters to see who finally killed the Canaanite commander, Sisera.

A WOMAN NAMED JAEL

5 ☐ **Pray.** ☐ **Read Judges 4:22-5:3.** ☐ **Think about what you read using the three keys on the inside front cover.**

Read the words from right to left to find out what happened after the battle.

enemies Israel's defeating for God praised that song a sang Barak and Deborah

▶ ☐ **Weekend Review**

Recite your memory verse to an adult. In your notebook, write about how God has given you courage and strength when you've faced troubles. Show it to a friend this week, and tell how God helps you.

WEEK 20 ☐ Memorize: 1 Samuel 3:19

1 ☐ **Pray.** ☐ **Read 1 Samuel 1:1-11.** ☐ **Think about what you read using the three keys on the inside front cover.**

To find out what Hannah promised God, read the darker words first and then the lighter ones.

If to **God** God **would** to **give** serve **her** God **a** for **son**, the **she** rest **would** of **give** his **him** life **back**

2 ☐ **Pray.** ☐ **Read 1 Samuel 1:12-20.** ☐ **Think about what you read using the three keys on the inside front cover.**

Write the numbers of the correct statements in the speech balloons.

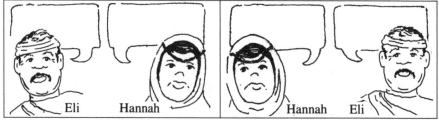

Eli   Hannah   Hannah   Eli

1. "I don't know how to pray to God." 2. "I'm not. I'm deeply troubled."
3. "May God give you what you asked." 4. "Stop getting drunk!"
5. "You should pray out loud." 6. "May God give you a long life."
7. "I'm sorry I cried." 8. "I've been praying because of my deep sadness."

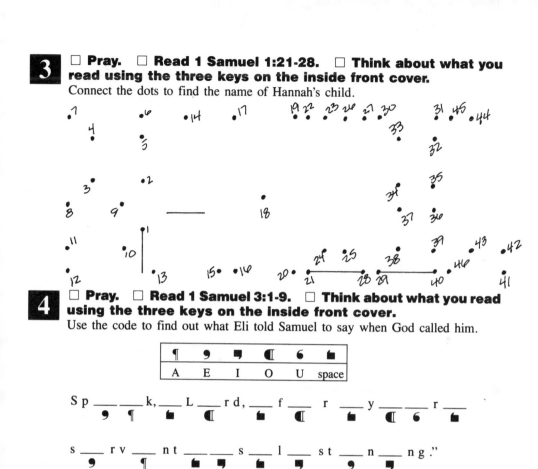

3

☐ **Pray.** ☐ **Read 1 Samuel 1:21-28.** ☐ **Think about what you read using the three keys on the inside front cover.**
Connect the dots to find the name of Hannah's child.

4

☐ **Pray.** ☐ **Read 1 Samuel 3:1-9.** ☐ **Think about what you read using the three keys on the inside front cover.**
Use the code to find out what Eli told Samuel to say when God called him.

¶	𝄞	◗	◖	6	◼
A	E	I	O	U	space

S p __ __ k, __ L __ r d, __ f __ r __ y __ __ r __
     𝄞   ¶   ◼   ◗   ◼   ◗   ◼   ◗ 6   ◼

s __ r v __ n t __ __ s __ l __ s t __ n __ n g ."
 𝄞   ¶   ◼ 𝄞   ◼ ¶   ◼ 𝄞   ¶

5

☐ **Pray.** ☐ **Read 1 Samuel 3:10-21.** ☐ **Think about what you read using the three keys on the inside front cover.**
To find out what happened to Samuel, cross out all the *B*s.

BGOBDBWABSWIBTBHBSABMUBELBABSBHBEGBREWBUBP
ABNBDBGBODBMADBEBALLBSABMUBEBBL'BSBMEBSBBS
ABGEBSBCOBMETBRUBEB

▶

☐ **Weekend Review**
Recite your memory verse to an adult. In your notebook, list two ways you can serve in your church, such as handing out bulletins or cleaning up pews after a service. This week, talk with your pastor or another adult in church about when and how you can serve.

☐ **Memorize: 1 Samuel 16:7b**

1 ☐ **Pray.** ☐ **Read 1 Samuel 15:10-23.** ☐ **Think about what you read using the three keys on the inside front cover.**
Use the code to find out what Samuel told King Saul.

A	B	C		M	N	O
D	E	F		P	R	S
G	H	I		T	V	Y

(coded message to be decoded)

2 ☐ **Pray.** ☐ **Read 1 Samuel 15:24-31.** ☐ **Think about what you read using the three keys on the inside front cover.**
Starting with *He*, cross out every other word to see what Samuel told King Saul.

He God will has reject taken all the place kingdom people of Saul Israel away from them you for and said given those it for to everyone someone around else.

3 ☐ **Pray.** ☐ **Read 1 Samuel 16:1-7.** ☐ **Think about what you read using the three keys on the inside front cover.**
To find out how God chooses people, write the correct letters from the grid on the blank lines.

A B C D E F G H I J K L M N O P Q R S T U V W X Y Z
(grid with marked points in rows 1-9)

___ ___ ___ ___ ___   ___ ___   ___ ___ ___   ___ ___ ___ ___ ___
 3   7   7   1   8   4   9   9   6   2   6   2   4   5   9

4 □ **Pray.** □ **Read 1 Samuel 16:8-13.** □ **Think about what you read using the three keys on the inside front cover.**

Check either the *yes* or *no* box for each statement about Samuel and David.

Yes   No

□   □   Jesse had six of his sons pass by Samuel.

□   □   David was taking care of sheep.

□   □   Everyone ate while waiting for David to come.

□   □   God told Samuel that David was his choice.

□   □   Samuel poured oil on David's brothers.

□   □   God's Spirit came on David after he grew up.

5 □ **Pray.** □ **Read 1 Samuel 16:17-23.** □ **Think about what you read using the three keys on the inside front cover.**

Write the first letters of the animals to find out what David did to help Saul.

___ ___ ___y___ ___   ___i___   ___a___ ___

▶ □ **Weekend Review**

Recite your memory verse to an adult. In your notebook, list three ways you can help in your community, such as by cleaning up litter or recycling. Choose one to do this week.

WEEK 22   □ **Memorize: 1 Samuel 18:3**

1 □ **Pray.** □ **Read 1 Samuel 18:1-16.** □ **Think about what you read using the three keys on the inside front cover.**

Do the puzzle about Jonathan, David, and King Saul.

Saul's son, __(7 Across), __(10 Down) David as much as he loved __(8 Across). Jonathan gave __(4 Down) his robe, tunic, __(13 Across), and __(3 Down). Everything David did pleased the __(5 Across). Women met Saul and David with __ (6 Down) and __(14 Across). Their song made Saul __(12 Across) and __(7 Down). When David played his __(1 Down), Saul __(11 Across) a __(15 Across) at him. The Lord was with David but left __(9 Down). Saul was __(2 Down) and sent David __(2 Across). David had __(6 Across) in everything he did.

2 □ **Pray.** □ **Read 1 Samuel 19:1-12.** □ **Think about what you read using the three keys on the inside front cover.**
Separate the letters into words to find out what Saul's son and daughter, Jonathan and Michal, did for David.

Jon at hans aid go odth in gstoh is fat herS aulab outDa vida ndMic ha lhe lpedD avi desc aped own outo faw in doww he nSa ulse ntmen toki llhim.

3 □ **Pray.** □ **Read 1 Samuel 20:1-11.** □ **Think about what you read using the three keys on the inside front cover.**
Circle the correct ending to the statement about Jonathan.

Jonathan said he would find out 1) how long the New Moon Festival would last. 2) why his father was angry with David. 3) his father's plans about David. 4) a way for David to return home safely. 5) how David's friends could help.

4 □ **Pray.** □ **Read 1 Samuel 20:12-23.** □ **Think about what you read using the three keys on the inside front cover.**
Use the code to find out what Jonathan said he would do to signal David.

5 □ **Pray.** □ **Read 1 Samuel 20:24-42.** □ **Think about what you read using the three keys on the inside front cover.**
Connect the dashes to see what Jonathan and David promised each other.

▶ □ **Weekend Review**
Recite your memory verse to an adult. This week, choose one way to show a friend how much you like being friends, such as doing something fun together, giving a small gift, or writing a note. Record what you did in your notebook.

1 ☐ **Pray.** ☐ **Read Matthew 18:1-9.** ☐ **Think about what you read using the three keys on the inside front cover.**
Cross out the capital letters to see who Jesus said is the greatest in the kingdom of heaven.

ToWn THe DAwN ShoW HiGH DREsS ALl SiTS LAke THaT SAcK ThiS Old

2 ☐ **Pray.** ☐ **Read Matthew 18:10-14.** ☐ **Think about what you read using the three keys on the inside front cover.**
Follow the straight lines to read how Jesus said the man who found the lost sheep felt.

3 ☐ **Pray.** ☐ **Read Matthew 18:15-20.** ☐ **Think about what you read using the three keys on the inside front cover.**
Do the math problems first. Fill in the correct letters to see what Jesus said.

1	2	3	4	5	6	7	8	9	10
a	e	g	h	m	n	o	r	t	w

$$
\begin{array}{cccccccc}
26 & 17 & 1 & 7 & 5 & 21 & 3 & 9 \\
-16 & -15 & +1 & +3 & +2 & -12 & +5 & -7 \\
\end{array}
$$

___ h ___ r ___ t ___ ___ or ___ h ___ ___ e

$$
\begin{array}{ccccccc}
5 & 44 & 3 & 15 & 17 & 4 & 48 \\
+4 & -41 & +6 & -7 & -11 & +1 & -46 \\
\end{array}
$$

come ___ o ___ e ___ he___ in my ___ a ___ ___,

$$
\begin{array}{cccccc}
13 & 37 & 6 & 2 & 9 & 37 \\
-9 & -35 & -4 & +7 & -5 & -32 \\
\end{array}
$$

I'm t ___ ___ r ___ with ___ ___ e ___.

4 ☐ **Pray.** ☐ **Read Matthew 18:21-27.** ☐ **Think about what you read using the three keys on the inside front cover.**
Cross out the wrong word in each pair from Jesus' story about forgiving others.

The **servant/kingdom** of heaven is like a king who decided to collect the money people owed him. One servant **owed/paid** him millions. **Nothing/Everything** the servant owned would have to be **sold/paid**, even the servant's **house/family**. The servant begged the king to be **patient/happy** with him. The king felt **angry/sorry** for the servant and told him he didn't have to **pay/sell** what he owed.

5 ☐ **Pray.** ☐ **Read Matthew 18:28-35.** ☐ **Think about what you read using the three keys on the inside front cover.**

Hold your book up to a mirror to see what Jesus said you should do.

FORGIVE OTHERS FROM YOUR HEART

▶ ☐ **Weekend Review**

Recite your memory verse to an adult. Create simple puppets (from paper lunch bags, Popsicle sticks, or socks) and use them to tell the story of the lost sheep or the unforgiving servant to a younger child this week.

WEEK 24 ☐ Memorize: John 11:25

1 ☐ **Pray.** ☐ **Read John 11:1-16.** ☐ **Think about what you read using the three keys on the inside front cover.**

Use the code to find out what Jesus told his followers.

a	e	i	o	u	space
◤	◢	◣	◪	⊠	⬛

◪⊠ r ⬛ f r ◢◤ n d ⬛ L ◤ z ◤ r ⬛ s ⬛◣ s ⬛ d ◢◤ d ⬛ .

2 ☐ **Pray.** ☐ **Read John 11:17-28.** ☐ **Think about what you read using the three keys on the inside front cover.**

Put the number of each quote in the speech balloon of the person who said it.

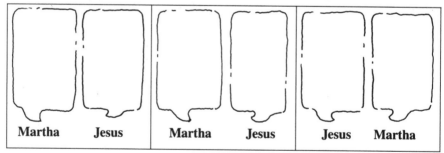

Martha   Jesus   Martha   Jesus   Jesus   Martha

1. "I know he'll live again at the resurrection."
2. "I believe you are the Christ, the Son of God."
3. "Your brother will rise and come to life again."
4. "If you'd been here, my brother wouldn't have died."
5. "I am the resurrection and the life."
6. "Do you believe this?"

☐ **Pray.** ☐ **Read John 11:29-37.** ☐ **Think about what you read using the three keys on the inside front cover.**
Cross out the words beginning with *C* to find out what Mary said to Jesus.

Can If cry cloud you'd come city been caring here circle coal, change my count brother captain couldn't cook wouldn't color clam have cured died clean cave.

☐ **Pray.** ☐ **Read John 11:38-44.** ☐ **Think about what you read using the three keys on the inside front cover.**
Finish the scene to show what happened after Jesus prayed and called to Lazarus.

☐ **Pray.** ☐ **Read John 11:45-57.** ☐ **Think about what you read using the three keys on the inside front cover.**
Use the code to find out what happened after Jesus made Lazarus come alive again.

A	B	C	D	E	F	G	H	I	J	K	L	M	N	O	P	Q	R	S	T	U	V	W	X	Y	Z
H	I	J	K	L	M	N	O	P	Q	R	S	T	U	V	W	X	Y	Z	A	B	C	D	E	F	G

FTGR   IXHIEX   UXEBXOXW   BG   CXLNL,   UNM

LHFX   IXHIEX   IETGGXW   MH   DBEE   ABF.

☐ **Weekend Review**
Recite your memory verse to an adult. In your notebook, write a coded message telling what you learned about Jesus' love and power this week. Give it to a friend to solve.

☐ **Memorize: Mark 16:15**

1 ☐ **Pray.** ☐ **Read Mark 15:1-15.** ☐ **Think about what you read using the three keys on the inside front cover.**

Starting with *He*, circle every third word to see what Pilate did with Jesus to please the crowd.

He did a gave pay time Jesus for by to men and soldiers so for to go or be taken a whipped by when and to a then put on killed to a on one man a to spot cross.

2 ☐ **Pray.** ☐ **Read Mark 15:16-32.** ☐ **Think about what you read using the three keys on the inside front cover.**

Use the code to find out what happened to Jesus.

✚	⚜	†	✛	✝	✜
a	e	i	o	u	space

S✚l d† ⚜r s✜n✚†l⚜d✜J⚜s†s✜t✝✜✚c r✚s s.✜T h⚜✜s†g n✜

✜n✜t h⚜✜c r✚s s✜s ✚†d✜"T h⚜✜K†n g✜✚f✜t h⚜✜J⚜w s."✜

P⚜✜p l⚜✜m✚c k⚜d✜J⚜s†s✜✚n d✜s✚†d,✜"S✚v⚜✜y✜tr s⚜l f!

✜C✚m⚜✜d✜w n✜f r✚m✜t h✚t✜c r✚s s !"

3 ☐ **Pray.** ☐ **Read Mark 15:33-47.** ☐ **Think about what you read using the three keys on the inside front cover.**

Mark the statements about Jesus' death *T* for *true* or *F* for *false*.

_____ At noon, darkness covered the whole country.

_____ Jesus cried out to Elijah.

_____ A man tried to give Jesus something to drink.

_____ Jesus cried in a loud voice before he died.

_____ The temple curtain split from side to side when Jesus died.

_____ The centurion who saw Jesus die said, "Surely this was an angel!"

_____ The women who followed Jesus didn't watch him die.

_____ Joseph of Arimathea asked Pilate for Jesus' body.

_____ Joseph put Jesus' body in a tomb and rolled a stone in front of the opening.

_____ Mary Magdalene and Mary didn't see where Jesus was buried.

4 ☐ **Pray.** ☐ **Read Mark 16:1-8.** ☐ **Think about what you read using the three keys on the inside front cover.**

To find out what the young man in a white robe told the women about Jesus, write down every other letter in the circle (use them all).

Start

___ ___ ___ , ___ ___

___ ___ ___ ___ ___

___ ___ ___ ___ ___ ___ !

5 ☐ **Pray.** ☐ **Read Mark 16:9-20.** ☐ **Think about what you read using the three keys on the inside front cover.**

Use the code to find out what Jesus told his followers to do.

🕯	✉	☎	☞	◯
a	e	i	o	space

G☞◯✉v✉rywh✉r✉◯☎n◯th✉◯w☞rld◯🕯nd◯t✉ll◯✉v

✉ry☞n✉◯th✉◯G☞☞rd◯N✉ws.

☐ Weekend Review

Recite your memory verse to an adult. Think about what Jesus' death and resurrection mean to you. Write this in your notebook, and talk about it with an adult this week.

WEEK 26 ☐ Memorize: Acts 4:12

1 ☐ **Pray.** ☐ **Read Acts 3:1-10.** ☐ **Think about what you read using the three keys on the inside front cover.**

Use the code to see what Peter told the crippled man who asked him for money.

$	+	−	±	÷	×	=	§	@	ᶜ	°	✔	#	®	©	%
B	D	F	G	H	J	K	L	M	N	P	R	S	T	V	W

I +oᶜ'® ÷a©e aᶜy @oᶜey, $u® I +o ÷a©e #o@e® ÷iᶜ± ®o

±i©e you. $y ® ÷e °o%e✔ o− ×e#u#'ᶜa @e, #®aᶜ+ uᶜaᶜ+ %a§=

2 ☐ **Pray.** ☐ **Read Acts 3:11-26.** ☐ **Think about what you read using the three keys on the inside front cover.**

Search for words from Peter's speech to the people.

beggar	killed	E	D	T	W	O	H	O	T	H	I	S	I	R	B

beggar   killed
Peter   raised
John   witnesses
people   sins
God   healing
Jesus   prophets
name   heaven
faith   blessed

```
E  D  T  W  O  H  O  T  H  I  S  I  R  B
H  A  O  E  S  E  S  S  E  N  T  I  W  L
T  B  E  G  G  A  R  A  A  C  E  O  N  E
I  S  K  I  L  L  E  D  V  S  H  I  N  S
A  U  D  E  S  I  A  R  E  A  P  H  O  S
F  S  E  M  A  N  O  O  N  Y  O  U  T  E
R  E  T  E  P  G  L  O  W  J  R  E  A  D
O  J  A  T  H  E  L  P  O  E  P  R  A  Y
```

3 ☐ **Pray.** ☐ **Read Acts 4:1-12.** ☐ **Think about what you read using the three keys on the inside front cover.**

Use the code to find out what Peter told the Jewish leaders.

①	②	③	④	⑤	⑥	⑦	⑧	⑨	⑩
A	B	D	E	J	M	S	T	U	V

We ⑥⑨⑦⑧ be ⑦①⑩④③ through ⑤④⑦⑨⑦

4 ☐ **Pray.** ☐ **Read Acts 4:13-22.** ☐ **Think about what you read using the three keys on the inside front cover.**

Read the capital letters to find out what Peter and John told the Jewish leaders.

oWEtCArN'ToKEbeEPrQUItET.WoEsMUdSiTesTaELmLABshOUT
aWHbATsWE'llVESbEENsANDtHEhARD.

5 ☐ **Pray.** ☐ **Read Acts 4:23-37.** ☐ **Think about what you read using the three keys on the inside front cover.**

Write the words from the believers' prayer where they belong on the puzzle.

WITHOUT   WORD   YOUR   HELP   FEAR   SPEAK   US

▶ ☐ **Weekend Review**

Recite your memory verse to an adult. Talk with friends this week about things you could do together to cheer up a sick person, such as baking a treat or performing a skit. List the ideas in your notebook, and plan to do one when a friend gets sick.

1   ☐ **Pray.**   ☐ **Read 1 Kings 16:29-34.**   ☐ **Think about what you read using the three keys on the inside front cover.**

Fill in the blanks. The circled letters form the name of a very wicked king.

He ruled Israel in ___ ◯ ___ ___ ___ ___ ___.

He built a temple and ___ ___ ___ ___ ◯ ___ ___ ___ ___ Baal.

He ___ ◯ ___ ___ ___ ___ ___ Jezebel, daughter of Ethbaal.

He sinned in the ways of ___ ___ ___ ___ ◯ ___ ___ ___, son of Nebat.

2   ☐ **Pray.**   ☐ **Read 1 Kings 17:1-6.**   ☐ **Think about what you read using the three keys on the inside front cover.**

Use the code to find out how God took care of Elijah at Kerith Ravine.

1	2	3	4	5	6	7	8	9	10	11	12	13	14	15	16	17	18	19	20	21	22	23	24	25	26
h	i	j	k	l	m	n	o	p	q	r	s	t	u	v	w	x	y	z	a	b	c	d	e	f	g

_____

11 20 15 24 7 12   21 11 8 14 26 1 13   1 2 6   21 11 24 20 23   20 7 23

_____

6 24 20 13   24 15 24 11 18   6 8 11 7 2 7 26   20 7 23   24 15 24 7 2 7 26

3   ☐ **Pray.**   ☐ **Read 1 Kings 17:7-12.**   ☐ **Think about what you read using the three keys on the inside front cover.**

To find out what Elijah asked and the widow answered, read the darker words first and then the lighter ones.

Please I **give** only **me** have **a** a **drink** handful **of** of **water** flour **and** and **a** a **piece** little **of** oil **bread.**

4   ☐ **Pray.**   ☐ **Read 1 Kings 17:13-16.**   ☐ **Think about what you read using the three keys on the inside front cover.**

Circle what God promised the widow if she did as Elijah said.

her land would always get rain   her jar would always have flour

her jug would always have oil   her son would always be well

her people would always like her   her name would always be famous

5 ☐ **Pray.**   ☐ **Read 1 Kings 17:17-24.**   ☐ **Think about what you read using the three keys on the inside front cover.**

Use the code to find out what Elijah prayed when the widow's son died.

a	△ e	◯ i	☆ o	✦ u

☆ L ☆ r d,   m y   G ☆ d,   l △ t   t h ◯ s

b ☆ y   l ◯ v △   ☐ g ☐ ◯ n !

▶ ☐ **Weekend Review**

Recite your memory verse to an adult. This week, make plans with friends or family to help people suffering from famine (for example, save lunch money to send food or to build wells). List ideas in your notebook and check those you do.

WEEK 28   ☐ Memorize: 2 Kings 4:33

1 ☐ **Pray.**   ☐ **Read 2 Kings 4:1-7.**   ☐ **Think about what you read using the three keys on the inside front cover.**

Use the code to find out what happened when the widow did what Elisha said to do.

A	D	E	F	H	I	J	L	M	N	O	R	S	Y
☺	☺	☺	☺	☺	☺	☺	☺	☺	☺	☺	☺	☺	☺

☺ ☺ ☺   🫕   ☺ ☺   ☺ ☺ ☺

☺ ☺ ☺ ☺ ☺ ☺   ☺ ☺ ☺ ☺   ☺ ☺ ☺ ☺

2
☐ **Pray.** ☐ **Read 2 Kings 4:8-21.** ☐ **Think about what you read using the three keys on the inside front cover.**
Start with the *Y*, and go from letter to letter. Write the letters on the lines to find out what Elisha promised the Shunammite woman who was kind to him.

```
    I    A      E        O
A ┌─────────────────────────┐ O
  │                         │
W │            Y            │ L
  │                         │
L └─────────────────────────┘ S
    H    V      N        U
```

Y _____
W _____
H _____
  _____
S _____

3
☐ **Pray.** ☐ **Read 2 Kings 4:22-37.** ☐ **Think about what you read using the three keys on the inside front cover.**
To see what happened to the Shunammite woman's son, cross out the wrong words.

When the woman's son died, she told **her husband/no one.** She saddled a **donkey/horse** and rode to **Elisha/Elijah.** He sent his **brother/servant** to put his **robe/staff** on the dead child. When the prophet came, he went into the room and **opened/shut** the door. He **prayed/shouted** and stretched himself out on the child. The child became **happy/warm, sneezed/laughed** seven times, and opened his eyes.

4
☐ **Pray.** ☐ **Read 2 Kings 4:38-41.** ☐ **Think about what you read using the three keys on the inside front cover.**
Separate the letters into words to find out what Elisha did to the poisoned stew.

Elishaputsomeflourinthepotandthenthefoodbecamegoodforthepeopletoeat

5
☐ **Pray.** ☐ **Read 2 Kings 4:42-44.** ☐ **Think about what you read using the three keys on the inside front cover.**
Put the correct numbers in the statements about what happened during a famine.

10 20 **30** 4O *50* 60 **70** 80 *90* 100

_____ loaves of bread fed _____ people.

▶
☐ **Weekend Review**
Recite your memory verse to an adult. This week, show hospitality to a new person in your school or church, such as by inviting that person home for a snack or to play a game. Write what you did and who you did it with in your notebook.

1 ☐ **Pray.** ☐ **Read Esther 1:1-12.** ☐ **Think about what you read using the three keys on the inside front cover.**

Find words from the story of a wealthy king.

Xerxes	palace	M	T	E	U	Q	N	A	B	E	C	A	L	A	P	H
throne	purple	O	R	N	U	T	U	N	E	S	C	R	O	W	N	T
banquet	silver	D	S	E	X	R	E	X	A	S	I	N	D	E	A	L
princes	gold	G	E	D	E	U	Q	P	U	R	P	L	E	X	T	A
nobles	queen	N	X	E	N	O	R	H	T	W	O	A	V	R	U	E
wealth	crown	I	R	A	N	G	E	R	Y	G	A	R	D	E	N	W
kingdom	beauty	K	I	T	N	O	B	L	E	S	E	C	N	I	R	P
garden	anger															

2 ☐ **Pray.** ☐ **Read Esther 1:13-22.** ☐ **Think about what you read using the three keys on the inside front cover.**

Read every other word to see what the wise men told the king he should do.

Choose one a old new girl queen by to be take the Queen King Vashti's to place.

3 ☐ **Pray.** ☐ **Read Esther 2:1-9.** ☐ **Think about what you read using the three keys on the inside front cover.**

Use the code to find out what Mordecai did for his cousin, Esther.

○	△	+	●	▲	✚	)	★	☆	✪	✳	✶	☆	✳	★	☆
A	C	D	E	F	G	H	I	K	N	O	R	S	T	U	W

) ●   ✳ ✳ ✳ ★   △ ○ ✶ ●   ✳ ▲   ) ● ✶   ○ ☆

) ★ ☆   ✳ ☆ ✪   + ○ ✶ ✚) ✳ ● ✶

4 ☐ **Pray.** ☐ **Read Esther 2:10-18.** ☐ **Think about what you read using the three keys on the inside front cover.**

Draw a ⬜ box around things the king gave when he made Esther queen.

sceptre   crown   horses   holiday   armies

gifts   throne   banquet   slaves   ships

5 □ **Pray.** □ **Read Esther 2:19-23.** □ **Think about what you read using the three keys on the inside front cover.**
Cross out the *F*s to find out what Mordecai overheard and warned Esther about.

FAFPFLOFTFBYFTWFOFDOFORFWAFYFGUFARFDFSFTOFFKFIFLLFTFHFEFFKFINFGF

▶ □ **Weekend Review**
Recite your memory verse to an adult. Choose someone to show your care to this week, such as a cousin, grandparent, or other relative. In your notebook, list your ideas, such as phoning, writing a note, or playing a game. Do one this week.

WEEK 30 □ Memorize: Esther 4:14b

1 □ **Pray.** □ **Read Esther 3:1-15.** □ **Think about what you read using the three keys on the inside front cover.**
Put the words in their spots to see what Haman asked the king to do because Mordecai the Jew would not bow to Haman.

an to
all the
on
one day write Jews
kill order

2 □ **Pray.** □ **Read Esther 4:1-8.** □ **Think about what you read using the three keys on the inside front cover.**
Use the code to find out what Mordecai asked Esther to do.

Z	Y	X	W	V	U	T	S	R	Q	P	O	N	M	L	K	J	I	H	G	F	E	D	C	B	A
A	B	C	D	E	F	G	H	I	J	K	L	M	N	O	P	Q	R	S	T	U	V	W	X	Y	Z

T L G L G S V P R M T Z M W Y V T S R N G L S Z E V

N V I X B Z M W H Z E V S V I K V L K O V, G S V Q V D H.

3 ☐ **Pray.** ☐ **Read Esther 4:9-17.** ☐ **Think about what you read using the three keys on the inside front cover.**
Unscramble the words to find out what Esther said to Mordecai.

Have the Jews give up **tagine** _____ and **krinding** _____

for three days and **stingh** _____. My **restvans** _____ and

I will do so, too. Then I'll go to the **gink** _____, even though I may

be **likedl** _____ because the law says no one may go to him

towhuti _____ being **delcal** _____ first.

4 ☐ **Pray.** ☐ **Read Esther 5:1-8.** ☐ **Think about what you read using the three keys on the inside front cover.**
Write the first letters of the objects to see what Esther asked the king and Haman to do.

___ ___ ___ ___   ___ ___ ___

___ ___ ___ q u ___ ___

5 ☐ **Pray.** ☐ **Read Esther 5:9-14.** ☐ **Think about what you read using the three keys on the inside front cover.**
Use the code to find out what Haman's wife and friends told him to do.

¶	9	◗	⟨	6	◼
A	E	I	O	U	space

B ___ ___ l d ___ ___ ___ ___ g ___ l l ___ ws ___ 75 ___ f ___ ___ t
   6 ◗   ◼ ¶ ◼ ¶   ⟨ ◼ ◼ 9 9

___ h ___ gh ___ ___ nd ___ ___ s k ___ t h ___ ___ ___ k ___ ng ___
◼ ◗ ◼ ¶ ◼ ¶ ◼ 9 ◼ ◗ ◼

t ___ ___ ___ h ___ v ___ ___ ___ M ___ r d ___ c ___ ___ ___ ___ ___ h ___ ng
⟨ ◼ ¶ 9 ◼ ⟨ 9 ¶ ◗ ◼ ¶

___ d ___ ___ ___ n ___ ___ ___ t.
9 ◼ ⟨ ◼ ◗

▶ ☐ **Weekend Review**
Recite your memory verse to an adult. Find out the names of your government officials, and write them in your notebook. With your family or friends, write one a letter telling your ideas of how to deal with a problem in your school or community.

1 ☐ **Pray.** ☐ **Read Esther 6:1-14.** ☐ **Think about what you read using the three keys on the inside front cover.**

Complete the puzzle about how the king honored Mordecai.

One _____ (7 Across) the king couldn't sleep. He had the record _____ (2 Across) read to him. It told how _____ (6 Across) had warned of a plot to kill the _____ (4 Down). The king asked Haman how to _____ (8 Across) someone. Haman said, "Put a royal _____ (1 Down) on him. Have him led through the _____ (5 Down) streets on a _____ (3 Across) that wears a _____ (1 Across) crest." The king ordered _____ (3 Down) to do this for Mordecai.

2 ☐ **Pray.** ☐ **Read Esther 7:1-10.** ☐ **Think about what you read using the three keys on the inside front cover.**

Read the words from right to left to see what Esther did at her second banquet.

people her kill to planned Haman how told and live her let to king the asked she

3 ☐ **Pray.** ☐ **Read Esther 8:1-6.** ☐ **Think about what you read using the three keys on the inside front cover.**

Match the statements with the right person.

Esther

the king

Mordecai

gave Mordecai a signet ring

begged the king to stop Haman's plan

put Mordecai in charge of Haman's things

came in to see the king

gave Esther all Haman's things

4 □ **Pray.** □ **Read Esther 8:7-10.** □ **Think about what you read using the three keys on the inside front cover.**

Use the code to find out what the king told Mordecai to write.

★	☆	✔	{	#	}	|	©	¶	†	□	■	‡	•	◄	§	%	►	@	●	'
A	B	C	D	E	F	G	H	I	J	K	L	N	O	R	S	T	U	W	Y	space

★ ‡ • % © # ◄ ' • ◄ { # ◄ ' § ★ ● ¶ ‡ \| ' % © # ' † # @ § '

✔ • ► ■ { ' } ¶ \| © % ' ☆ ★ ✔ □

5 □ **Pray.** □ **Read Esther 8:11-17.** □ **Think about what you read using the three keys on the inside front cover.**

Follow the strings to the letters to see what the thirteenth day of the twelfth month became a time of for the Jews.

► □ **Weekend Review**

Recite your memory verse to an adult. In your notebook, write a plan of how your family can celebrate a holiday or special family event. Use this plan for your next family celebration.

WEEK 32 □ Memorize: Acts 7:55

1 □ **Pray.** □ **Read Acts 6:1-7.** □ **Think about what you read using the three keys on the inside front cover.**

Do the math problems, and blacken all spaces except those with the answer 7. The letters that are left spell the name of one of the seven men chosen to serve.

$8 - 2$	$3 + 4$	$6 + 5$	$13 - 6$	$4 + 5$	$14 - 8$	$13 - 6$
A	S	I	T	O	M	E
$11 - 4$	$12 - 7$	$6 + 1$	$3 + 5$	$10 - 3$	$5 + 2$	$15 - 9$
P	O	H	K	E	N	T

2 ☐ **Pray.** ☐ **Read Acts 6:8-11.** ☐ **Think about what you read using the three keys on the inside front cover.**

Starting with *They,* read every third word to find out about Stephen's words.

They talked told were hard good wise for but and angry strange strong happy.

3 ☐ **Pray.** ☐ **Read Acts 6:12-15.** ☐ **Think about what you read using the three keys on the inside front cover.**

Read the words made up of large and small letters to see what Stephen's face looked like.

I K E H E T C E A F A N G E L N

4 ☐ **Pray.** ☐ **Read Acts 7:1-2, 51-53.** ☐ **Think about what you read using the three keys on the inside front cover.**

Use the code to find out what Stephen said to the Jewish leaders.

①	❶	②	❷	③	❸	④	❹	⑤	❺	⑥	❻	⑦	❼	⑧	❽	⑨	❾	⑩	❿	Ⓒ
a	b	c	d	e	g	h	i	k	l	m	n	o	p	r	s	t	u	w	y	space

_____ _____ _____ _____ _____ _____ _____ _____ **!**
⑩⑦⑨Ⓒ⑧⑨❾❶❶⑦⑧⑥Ⓒ⑤❸①❷③❽⑧ Ⓒ⑩⑦⑨⑧Ⓒ①⑥❷③❽⑨

_____ _____ _____ _____ _____ _____ _____
⑦⑧❽Ⓒ④❾⑧⑨Ⓒ⑨④❸Ⓒ❼⑧⑦❼④❸⑨⑧Ⓒ⑩④⑦⑨⑦❺❷Ⓒ⑨④

_____ _____ _____ _____ _____ **(Jesus)**
①⑨Ⓒ⑨④❸Ⓒ⑧❹❷❸④⑨❷⑦⑨⑧Ⓒ⑦❻❸Ⓒ ⑩⑦⑨❺❷Ⓒ②⑦❻

_____ _____ _____ _____ **.**
❸ Ⓒ①❻❷Ⓒ⑩⑦⑨Ⓒ⑤❹❺❺❸❷②④❹❻

5 ☐ **Pray.** ☐ **Read Acts 7:54-60.** ☐ **Think about what you read using the three keys on the inside front cover.**

Circle the things that Stephen said.

"Receive my spirit, Lord Jesus!"

"Lord, don't hold this sin against them!"

"Lord, punish these sinners!"

"You're all telling lies!"

"Lord, show them the vision of heaven!"

"I see Jesus in heaven at God's right side!"

▶ ☐ **Weekend Review**

Recite your memory verse to an adult. In your notebook, write a coded message telling what you believe about Jesus. Give it to a friend to solve. Then talk together about Jesus.

1 ☐ **Pray.** ☐ **Read Acts 9:32-43.** ☐ **Think about what you read using the three keys on the inside front cover.**

In the triangle, find the names of two people Peter healed. Starting with *T*, write the darker letters. Then write the lighter letters.

— — — — — — — — — —

— — — — — — —

2 ☐ **Pray.** ☐ **Read Acts 10:1-8.** ☐ **Think about what you read using the three keys on the inside front cover.**

Follow the words through the maze to see what the angel told Cornelius to do.

3 ☐ **Pray.** ☐ **Read Acts 10:9-23.** ☐ **Think about what you read using the three keys on the inside front cover.**

Finish the picture to show what Peter saw in his vision.

4 ☐ **Pray.** ☐ **Read Acts 10:24-33.** ☐ **Think about what you read using the three keys on the inside front cover.**

Separate the letters into words to see who was waiting for Peter in Caesarea.

Corneliusthearmyofficerandhisfamilyandhisclosefriends

5 ☐ **Pray.** ☐ **Read Acts 10:34-48.** ☐ **Think about what you read using the three keys on the inside front cover.**

Use the code to see what Peter told Cornelius and the other non-Jewish people.

✚	⬦	✝	✢	✝	✛
a	e	i	o	u	space

✚l l✛p⬦ ✢p l⬦✛w h✢✛b⬦l✝ ⬦v⬦✛ ✝ n✛J⬦s✝s✛w ✝l l✛

b⬦✛f✢r g✝v⬦n

▶ ☐ **Weekend Review**

Recite your memory verse to an adult. This week, learn about a group of people who have never heard about Jesus. Ask your parents, pastor, and others from your church for information. Write what you find out in your notebook, and then pray for the group.

WEEK 34   ☐ **Memorize: Acts 16:31**

1 ☐ **Pray.** ☐ **Read Acts 16:1-5.** ☐ **Think about what you read using the three keys on the inside front cover.**

Shade in the squares marked with only one line to see who Paul took with him.

2 ☐ **Pray.** ☐ **Read Acts 16:6-10.** ☐ **Think about what you read using the three keys on the inside front cover.**

Use the code to find out what Paul saw in a vision.

↙	↘	↑	↓	↕	↙↗	↘	✦	✦	♦	•—	⚬ᵒ	⚬ᵒ	⚬—⚬	⚬	⚬	⚬
A	C	D	E	F	H	I	L	M	N	O	P	R	S	T	U	V	space

(coded message)

3 □ **Pray.** □ **Read Acts 16:11-15.** □ **Think about what you read using the three keys on the inside front cover.**

Fill in the blanks. The letters in squares are the name of a person who listened to Paul and believed in Jesus.

This person had a job selling ___ ___ ___ ___ ☐ ___ cloth.

This person asked Paul and his friends to ___ ___ ___ ☐ in her house.

This person worshiped ___ ___ ☐ .

This person met with other women by the ___ ☐ ___ ___ ___ .

This person and people in her house were ___ ☐ ___ ___ ___ ___ ___ ___ .

4 □ **Pray.** □ **Read Acts 16:16-24.** □ **Think about what you read using the three keys on the inside front cover.**

Use the code to find out what the slave girl said about Paul and Silas.

†	‡	#	§	¶	•
a	e	i	o	u	space

Th‡y•†r‡•s‡rv†nts•§f•th‡•M§st•H#gh•G§d •Th‡y•†r‡•t‡ll#ng•

y§¶•h§w•t§•b‡•s†v‡d.

5 □ **Pray.** □ **Read Acts 16:25-40.** □ **Think about what you read using the three keys on the inside front cover.**

For each statement about Paul and Silas, check either the *yes* or *no* box.

Yes No

☐ ☐ At midnight they preached to the other prisoners.

☐ ☐ An earthquake trapped them in the prison building.

☐ ☐ They told the jailer not to kill himself because no one had escaped.

☐ ☐ The jailer asked them, "What must I do to be saved?"

☐ ☐ They told him to believe on Jesus to be saved.

☐ ☐ Their wounds were washed by the other prisoners.

☐ ☐ They spent the night in the jailer's house.

☐ ☐ In the morning, officers took them back to jail.

▶ □ **Weekend Review**

Recite your memory verse to an adult. Plan and lead a family prayer or devotional time this week, perhaps at a meal or bedtime. Write what you plan to do in your notebook, and put a check by it when you've done it.

1 ☐ **Pray.** ☐ **Read Acts 21:17-26.** ☐ **Think about what you read using the three keys on the inside front cover.**

Follow the maze to find out where Paul went to show he followed the law of Moses.

Jordan River

Start →

Rome

James' house

Temple

2 ☐ **Pray.** ☐ **Read Acts 21:27-36.** ☐ **Think about what you read using the three keys on the inside front cover.**

Use the code to find out what happened when Paul was about to be beaten to death.

a	e	i	o	u	space

Th ◲◩ c ◰ mm ◳ nd ◱ r ◩◰ f ◩ R ◰ m ◳ n ◩ t r ◰◰ p s ◩

◳ nd ◩ h ◰ s ◩ s ◰ ld ◰◱ r s ◩ c ◳ m ◲◩, s t ◰ p p ◳ d ◩

th ◲◩ b ◳◲ t ◰ ng ◩, ◳ nd ◩◲ r r ◳ s t ◳ d ◩ P ◲◩ l.

3 ☐ **Pray.** ☐ **Read Acts 21:37-22:5.** ☐ **Think about what you read using the three keys on the inside front cover.**

To see what Paul asked the Roman commander, cross out words that start with *W.*

who wanted to work well talk when to which the women who were people where

4 ☐ **Pray.** ☐ **Read Acts 22:6-21.** ☐ **Think about what you read using the three keys on the inside front cover.**

Do the crossword puzzle about how Paul came to believe in Jesus.

About ____ (10 Across), as Paul was on his way to Damascus, a bright ____ (4 Across) from ____ (8 Across) flashed on him. He fell to the ____ (5 Down). A ____ (9 Down) said, "Why are you persecuting me?" Paul asked, "Who are you, ____ (4 Down)?" "I am ____ (6 Down) of Nazareth." He told Paul to go to ____ (11 Across). Paul was ____ (7 Down) from the light. ____ (2 Down) came to him and said, "____ (7 Across) Saul, see again!" He said God had ____ (3 Down) Paul to be his ____ (1 Down) to all people.

5 ☐ **Pray.** ☐ **Read Acts 22:22-30.** ☐ **Think about what you read using the three keys on the inside front cover.**

Hold your book up to a mirror to read why the Roman soldiers did not beat Paul.

BECAUSEHEWASAROMANCITIZEN

▶ ☐ **Weekend Review**

Recite your memory verse to an adult. This week, ask an older person about how he or she came to believe in Jesus. Write their story in your notebook.

WEEK 36 ☐ Memorize: Acts 27:25

1 ☐ **Pray.** ☐ **Read Acts 27:1-12.** ☐ **Think about what you read using the three keys on the inside front cover.**

Search for words from the story of Paul's trip.

sail	Myra	A	P	O	U	R	E	T	N	I	W	S	A	Y	S	S	T	A	B
Italy	Cyprus	W	O	F	S	U	N	L	O	T	W	I	N	E	C	R	E	T	E
Paul	wind	A	S	R	E	N	O	S	I	R	P	D	N	A	Y	E	A	A	R
sea	prisoners	Y	T	H	P	A	N	E	T	A	F	O	R	D	P	A	R	Y	M
Julius	Crete	M	E	E	I	N	E	T	U	M	S	N	E	A	R	F	I	R	E
ship	harbor	I	N	S	O	P	Y	L	A	T	I	N	N	J	U	L	I	U	S
Asia	winter	H	A	R	B	O	R	X	I	N	E	O	H	P	S	H	O	P	S
Sidon	Phoenix

2 ☐ **Pray.** ☐ **Read Acts 27:13-26.** ☐ **Think about what you read using the three keys on the inside front cover.**

Read only the capital letters to find out what the angel told Paul.

wHEnfeWOodULlDuSTyANtsDoTeRImsALtBEeFrOmReEdCarAsEarSoApuRe

3 ☐ **Pray.** ☐ **Read Acts 27:27-38.** ☐ **Think about what you read using the three keys on the inside front cover.**

Use the code to find out what Paul told the people on the ship just before dawn.

4
☐ **Pray.** ☐ **Read Acts 27:39-44.** ☐ **Think about what you read using the three keys on the inside front cover.**
Number the events of the shipwreck in the correct order.

_____ The ship hit a sandbar.

_____ Julius ordered everyone to swim or float to land.

_____ The sailors cut the anchors loose and raised the sail.

_____ The sailors saw a beach at daylight.

_____ All the people made it safely to land.

_____ The ship was stuck.

_____ The sailors sailed the ship toward the beach.

_____ The waves began to break up the back of the ship.

_____ The soldiers decided to kill all the prisoners.

5
☐ **Pray.** ☐ **Read Acts 28:1-10.** ☐ **Think about what you read using the three keys on the inside front cover.**
Blacken out the Xs to find out what the people thought when a snake bit Paul.

▶ ☐ **Weekend Review**
Recite your memory verse to an adult. This week, set up a simple obstacle course for a younger child to enjoy. Then tell the child how God helped Paul in his travels.

1 □ **Pray.** □ **Read Psalm 23:1-6.** □ **Think about what you read using the three keys on the inside front cover.**

Fit the words from Psalm 23 into the phrase *the Lord is my Shepherd.*

rest   pastures   water   soul   paths   shadow   name   rod   staff   table
head   cup   goodness   love   days   life   dwell   house   forever

```
                                      T        W
 P          S                    P __       L _ G
 _      _ F          N D      R _ _ C       _ _ _
 _ S H   _ R _      L         _ _       _ _ _ _   _ _ _
 T H E   L O R D   I S   M Y   S H E P H E R D
 _ _ _   _ _ _   _ _   _ _   _ _   _       _
 _ _ _   _ _ _   _ _             _       _
 _ _     _ _ _   _               _       _
 _ _     _ _ _   _               _       _
```

2 □ **Pray.** □ **Read Psalm 27:1-14.** □ **Think about what you read using the three keys on the inside front cover.**

Use the sounds of the objects to find out what the psalmist asked God.

1 t h + – r ask: **2** d + in the

of the L + – s w **4** +ever

3 □ **Pray.** □ **Read Psalm 34:1-10.** □ **Think about what you read using the three keys on the inside front cover.**

Read the capital letters only to see what the psalmist said.

TheArmiSToEshANDmuStEEnTenHowArTleGsOmeDayInnSayGrOwnOverDo

4 □ **Pray.** □ **Read Psalm 34:11-22.** □ **Think about what you read using the three keys on the inside front cover.**

Match the phrases to what the psalmist said.

Keep your tongue	from evil.
Keep your lips	to the cries of good people.
Turn away	to the brokenhearted.
Do	from saying evil things.
Seek	good people from their troubles.
God sees	people who do evil.
God listens	righteous people.
God is against	good things.
God saves	from telling lies.
God is close	peace.

5 ☐ **Pray.** ☐ **Read Psalm 121:1-8.** ☐ **Think about what you read using the three keys on the inside front cover.**

Fill in the letters to see what the psalmist said God will do.

WATCH OVER YOUR LIFE

▶ ☐ **Weekend Review**

Recite your memory verse to an adult. In your notebook, write your own psalm to God. Read it to a family member or friend this week.

WEEK 38   ☐ Memorize: Psalm 100:3

1 ☐ **Pray.** ☐ **Read Psalm 100:1-5.** ☐ **Think about what you read using the three keys on the inside front cover.**

Use the code to find out what the psalmist said to do.

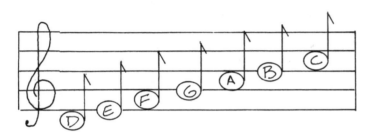

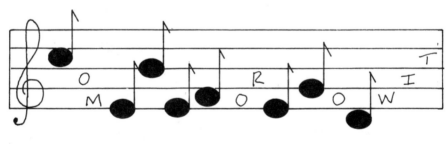

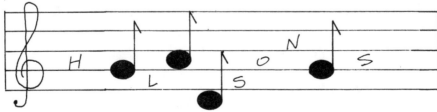

2 ☐ **Pray.** ☐ **Read Psalm 139:1-6.** ☐ **Think about what you read using the three keys on the inside front cover.**

To see what the psalmist told God, read the darker words first and then the lighter ones.

O before **God** I you say **have** a **searched** word **me** you **and** know **you** it **know** all **me**

3 ☐ **Pray.** ☐ **Read Psalm 139:7-12.** ☐ **Think about what you read using the three keys on the inside front cover.**
Cross out all the Ys to find out what the psalmist said about God.

Y Day ryy kyn eyssy iysyty yheysy aymeyyaysy ly igy hyytyty oyhyyiyyymy.

4 ☐ **Pray.** ☐ **Read Psalm 139:13-18.** ☐ **Think about what you read using the three keys on the inside front cover.**
Search for words from the psalm.

created	body	I	S	T	H	G	U	O	H	T	A	K	E	N	O	W	S
being	days	D	U	O	L	U	F	R	E	D	N	O	W	E	E	D	O
mother	book	M	O	T	H	E	R	E	D	U	F	O	G	I	V	E	N
praise	precious	A	I	G	R	A	I	N	S	E	R	B	R	N	O	T	E
made	thoughts	D	C	O	S	Y	A	D	O	K	A	R	O	B	I	A	S
works	God	E	E	R	E	S	T	S	S	A	M	E	W	D	O	E	R
wonderful	grains	N	R	O	A	M	E	A	T	W	E	D	S	A	Y	R	B
frame	sand	S	P	R	A	I	S	E	O	A	T	S	R	E	A	C	H
eyes	awake														

5 ☐ **Pray.** ☐ **Read Psalm 139:19-24.** ☐ **Think about what you read using the three keys on the inside front cover.**
Use the code to find out what the psalmist wanted God to do.

A	E	I	O	U	Y	space
♥	♥	♥	♥	♥	♥	♥

___ ___ G ___ d , ___ s ___ ___ r c h ___ m ___ ___ ___ n d

k n ___ w ___ m ___ ___ h ___ ___ r t.

☐ **Weekend Review**
Recite your memory verse to an adult. This week, get together with friends and practice a song praising God or put the psalm you wrote last week to music. Then sing it for others, such as younger children in Sunday school or older people in a retirement center. Record what you did in your notebook.

1 ☐ **Pray.** ☐ **Read Proverbs 15:1-13.** ☐ **Think about what you read using the three keys on the inside front cover.**

In the circles, draw happy or sad faces to show what Proverbs says about each.

◯ gentle answer　　◯ wise words　　◯ unkind answer

◯ rejecting a parent's correction　　◯ way of the wicked

◯ happy heart　　◯ healing words　　◯ deceitful words

2 ☐ **Pray.** ☐ **Read Proverbs 15:14-26.** ☐ **Think about what you read using the three keys on the inside front cover.**

Follow the line through the words to read the proverb.

angry　gets　trouble　but　patient　controls　a
who　person　stirs　a　is　and　temper　down
Start → A　quickly　up　person　who　his　calms　quarrel

3 ☐ **Pray.** ☐ **Read Proverbs 15:27-16:6.** ☐ **Think about what you read using the three keys on the inside front cover.**

Read the sentence from right to left to read the proverb.

succeed will plans your then and do you whatever God to Commit

4 ☐ **Pray.** ☐ **Read Proverbs 16:7-19.** ☐ **Think about what you read using the three keys on the inside front cover.**

Use the code to find out what the proverb says is important.

Code:
- A (top) / D (left) B (right) / C (bottom)
- E (top) / I (left) G (right) / H (bottom)
- L (top) / K (left) M (right) / N (bottom)
- O (top) / T (left) R (right) / S (bottom)
- U (top) / space (left) V (right) / W (bottom)

"BETTER A LITTLE WITH THE FEAR OF THE LORD THAN GREAT WEALTH WITH TURMOIL"

5 ☐ **Pray.** ☐ **Read Proverbs 16:20-33.** ☐ **Think about what you read using the three keys on the inside front cover.**
Cross out words beginning with *H* to read the proverb.

he holy whoever helps trusts in God heaven hopes will be healthy blessed hope.

▶ ☐ **Weekend Review**
Recite your memory verse to an adult. This week, draw your own maze using the words of a proverb, and give it to a friend to do. Then talk together about following God's ways.

WEEK 40 ☐ Memorize: Isaiah 55:8

1 ☐ **Pray.** ☐ **Read Isaiah 55:1-2.** ☐ **Think about what you read using the three keys on the inside front cover.**
Do the crossword puzzle about what God said.

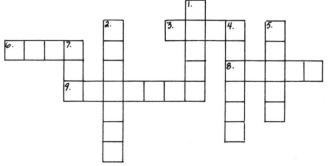

God says, "Come, all who are ____(9 Across), ____(6 Across) and drink. You who don't have ____(1 Down), come, buy and ____(7 Down). Why ____(8 Across) your money on what isn't ____(5 Down)? Why work for what doesn't ____(2 Down)? ____(4 Down) to me and your ____(3 Across) will enjoy rich food."

2 ☐ **Pray.** ☐ **Read Isaiah 55:3-5.** ☐ **Think about what you read using the three keys on the inside front cover.**
Starting with *Listen*, circle every other word to read what God asks.

Listen come to be me them so when your people soul stays will be live good

3 ☐ **Pray.** ☐ **Read Isaiah 55:6-7.** ☐ **Think about what you read using the three keys on the inside front cover.**
Use the code to find out what the prophet Isaiah said to do.

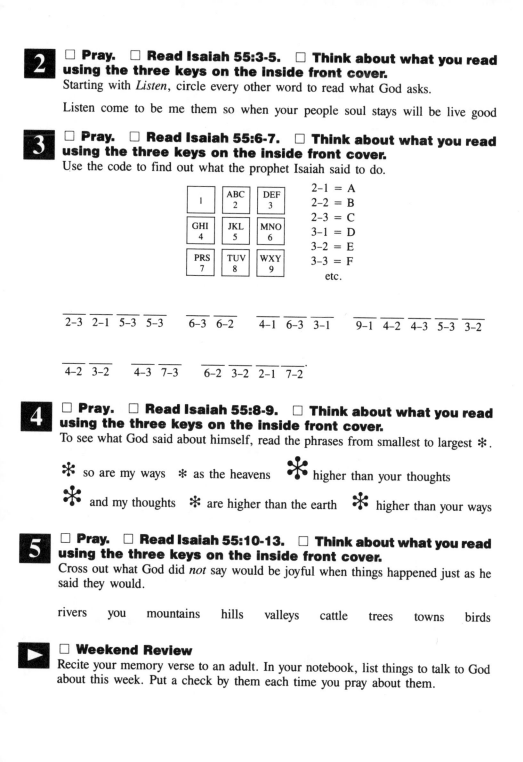

	ABC 2	DEF 3
GHI 4	JKL 5	MNO 6
PRS 7	TUV 8	WXY 9

2–1 = A
2–2 = B
2–3 = C
3–1 = D
3–2 = E
3–3 = F
etc.

‾2‾-3 ‾2‾-1 ‾5‾-3 ‾5‾-3   ‾6‾-3 ‾6‾-2   ‾4‾-1 ‾6‾-3 ‾3‾-1   ‾9‾-1 ‾4‾-2 ‾4‾-3 ‾5‾-3 ‾3‾-2

‾4‾-2 ‾3‾-2   ‾4‾-3 ‾7‾-3   ‾6‾-2 ‾3‾-2 ‾2‾-1 ‾7‾-2.

4 ☐ **Pray.** ☐ **Read Isaiah 55:8-9.** ☐ **Think about what you read using the three keys on the inside front cover.**
To see what God said about himself, read the phrases from smallest to largest ✳.

✳ so are my ways   ✳ as the heavens   ✳ higher than your thoughts

✳ and my thoughts   ✳ are higher than the earth   ✳ higher than your ways

5 ☐ **Pray.** ☐ **Read Isaiah 55:10-13.** ☐ **Think about what you read using the three keys on the inside front cover.**
Cross out what God did *not* say would be joyful when things happened just as he said they would.

rivers   you   mountains   hills   valleys   cattle   trees   towns   birds

▶ ☐ **Weekend Review**
Recite your memory verse to an adult. In your notebook, list things to talk to God about this week. Put a check by them each time you pray about them.

1 □ **Pray.** □ **Read Romans 12:1-2.** □ **Think about what you read using the three keys on the inside front cover.**
Write in the words from the correct puzzle piece to see what Paul said to do.

1) Don't conform any longer

2) to the world's pattern

4) by a new way of thinking

4) by copying good people

3) but be changed

4) by doing good deeds

4) by trying to be kind

2 □ **Pray.** □ **Read Romans 12:3-8.** □ **Think about what you read using the three keys on the inside front cover.**
Use the code to find out what Paul said about Christians.

✚	♱	†	✛	†	✛
a	e	i	o	u	space

W♱'r♱ ✚ ✚l l ✚ ✛n♱ ✚b✛d y ✚ † n ✚C h r † s t ✛. ♱ ✚c h ✚b♱

l ✛n g s ✚t ✛ ✚ t h♱ ✚✛ t h ♱ r s ✚ W♱ ✚ ✚l l ✚ h ✚v ♱ ✚

d † f f ♱r ♱ n t ✚g † f t s.

3 □ **Pray.** □ **Read Romans 12:9-13.** □ **Think about what you read using the three keys on the inside front cover.**
Circle the correct word in each pair.

Love must be **happy/real**. **Hate/Fight** what is evil but hold on to what is **costly/good**. **Honor/Help** each other more than yourselves. Serve God with all your **talents/heart**. Be **thankful/joyful** in hope and be **patient/careful** when trouble comes. **Work/Pray** faithfully. Share with God's people who are **kind/needy**.

4 □ **Pray.** □ **Read Romans 12:14-16.** □ **Think about what you read using the three keys on the inside front cover.**
Starting with *p*, cross out every third letter to see what Paul said to do.

L i p v e t i n s p e t a c k e w e i t s h o t n e t a n k o t s h e e r

5 ☐ **Pray.** ☐ **Read Romans 12:17-21.** ☐ **Think about what you read using the three keys on the inside front cover.**

Mark the sentences either *Do* or *Don't*.

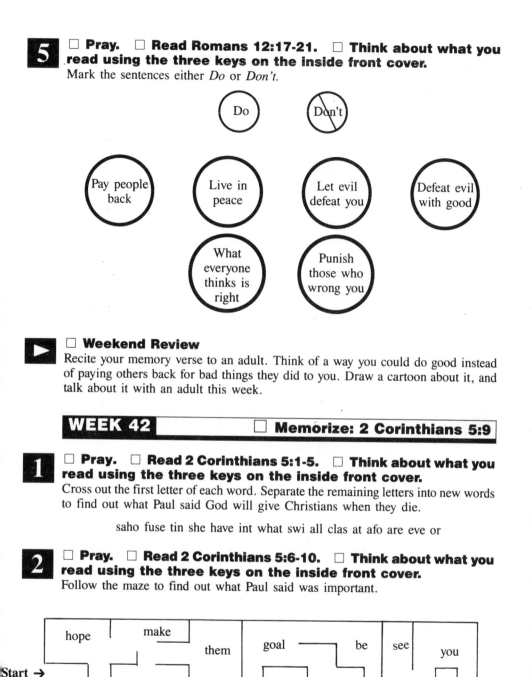

▶ ☐ **Weekend Review**

Recite your memory verse to an adult. Think of a way you could do good instead of paying others back for bad things they did to you. Draw a cartoon about it, and talk about it with an adult this week.

WEEK 42 ☐ Memorize: 2 Corinthians 5:9

1 ☐ **Pray.** ☐ **Read 2 Corinthians 5:1-5.** ☐ **Think about what you read using the three keys on the inside front cover.**

Cross out the first letter of each word. Separate the remaining letters into new words to find out what Paul said God will give Christians when they die.

saho fuse tin she have int what swi all clas at afo are eve or

2 ☐ **Pray.** ☐ **Read 2 Corinthians 5:6-10.** ☐ **Think about what you read using the three keys on the inside front cover.**

Follow the maze to find out what Paul said was important.

3 ☐ **Pray.**   ☐ **Read 2 Corinthians 9:6-8.**   ☐ **Think about what you read using the three keys on the inside front cover.**

Use the code to find out what Paul said about giving.

C	E	F	G	H	I	L	N	O	R	S	U	V	Y
☺	☺	☺	☺	☺	☺	☺	☺	☺	☺	☺	☺	☺	☺

God _ _ _ _ _ the _ _ _ who

_ _ _ _ _   _ _ _ _ _ _ _ _ _ _

4 ☐ **Pray.**   ☐ **Read 2 Corinthians 9:9-11.**   ☐ **Think about what you read using the three keys on the inside front cover.**

Cross out the $s to see what Paul said.

$Go$$dw$ill$$makeyour$$ichineverywaysoyouc$anb$$ege$nero$us$ too$$the$rs.

5 ☐ **Pray.**   ☐ **Read 2 Corinthians 9:12-15.**   ☐ **Think about what you read using the three keys on the inside front cover.**

Write the words from the correct pieces in the gift box to read Paul's statement.

THANKS

JESUS

GOD

HIS   BY

GIFT   BE TO   ALL   FOR

INDESCRIBABLE

▶ ☐ **Weekend Review**

Recite your memory verse to an adult. In your notebook, write a plan of what amount of money you want to give regularly for God's work. Starting with this week, record your giving in your notebook.

☐ **Memorize: Ephesians 2:8**

1

☐ **Pray.** ☐ **Read Ephesians 2:1-5.** ☐ **Think about what you read using the three keys on the inside front cover.**

Use the code to find out why God sent Jesus Christ to save us.

A	E	G	H	I	L	O	R	S	T	U	V
♥	♥	♥	♥	♥	♥	♥	♥	♥	♥	♥	♥

Because of ♥♥♥ ♥♥♥♥♥ ♥♥♥♥

for ♥♥

2

☐ **Pray.** ☐ **Read Ephesians 2:6-10.** ☐ **Think about what you read using the three keys on the inside front cover.**

Do the crossword puzzle about salvation.

You've been ___(5 Across) by ___(2 Down) through faith. This isn't from ___(7 Across). It's God's ___(2 Across) so no one can ___(4 Down) about it. We're ___ (1 Down) workmanship, created in ___(3 Down) Christ to do good ___(6 Across).

3

☐ **Pray.** ☐ **Read Ephesians 2:11-13.** ☐ **Think about what you read using the three keys on the inside front cover.**

Separate the letters into words to find out Paul's reminder to believers.

RememberyouwereonceseparatefromGodbutnowyou'vebeenbroughtneartohimthroughChrist.

4

☐ **Pray.** ☐ **Read Ephesians 2:14-18.** ☐ **Think about what you read using the three keys on the inside front cover.**

Use the code to find out what Paul said Jesus did.

#	☐	%	@	●
A	E	I	O	U

J ___ s ___ s m ___ d ___ J ___ w s & n ___ n-J ___ w s
  ☐   ●   #   ☐   ☐   @   ☐

b ___ c ___ m ___ ___ n ___ n ___ w p ___ ___ pl ___
  ☐ @ ☐   @ ☐   ☐   ☐ @   ☐

___ n h ___ m
%   %

☐ **Pray.** ☐ **Read Ephesians 2:19-22.** ☐ **Think about what you read using the three keys on the inside front cover.**

Read the uncracked bricks to see what Christians are being built into together.

a	holy	place	work	for
in	to	which	God	has	lives
told	by	every	his	our	Spirit	way

▶ ☐ **Weekend Review**

Recite your memory verse to an adult. In your notebook, write what you've learned about God's love this week. Talk about it with a family member or friend.

WEEK 44   ☐ **Memorize: Colossians 3:17**

1 ☐ **Pray.** ☐ **Read Colossians 3:1-4.** ☐ **Think about what you read using the three keys on the inside front cover.**

Use the code to find out what Paul said to do.

a	e	i	o	u	w	y	space
◐	◑	◖	◗	◔	◕	●	○

S ◐ t ○ ● ◖ ◗ r ○ h ◐ ◑ r t s ○ ◑ n d ○ m ◖ n d s

○ ◖ n ○ t h ◖ n g s ○ ◑ b ◖ v ◐ ○ n ◖ t ○ ◖ n ○

◑ ◐ r t h l ● ○ t h ◖ n g s

2 ☐ **Pray.** ☐ **Read Colossians 3:5-11.** ☐ **Think about what you read using the three keys on the inside front cover.**

Hold your book up to a mirror to read what Paul said Christians put on.

ƎƆAMIꙄ'ᗡOᎮИIƎᗡAMᎮИIƎꓭꙄIHƆIHWꟻꙄƎWꟻИA

3 □ **Pray.** □ **Read Colossians 3:12-14.** □ **Think about what you read using the three keys on the inside front cover.**
Search for words from the verses about how to act with other people.

gentleness	chosen	
people	patience	
holy	bear	
loved	each	
clothe	other	
compassion	forgive	
kindness	Lord	
humility	unity	

```
E  S  S  E  N  D  N  I  K  I  D  S  H  A  K  E
C  H  O  S  E  N  R  R  T  O  P  A  D  O  T  E  N
N  O  I  S  S  A  P  M  O  C  L  E  A  N  S  Y  U
E  T  T  R  E  E  L  E  A  L  V  A  N  H  O  E  N
I  A  A  B  T  P  A  S  N  O  W  I  N  G  O  T  I
T  R  C  S  S  E  N  E  L  T  N  E  G  B  E  L  T
A  O  T  H  E  R  S  A  T  H  U  M  I  L  I  T  Y
P  E  O  P  L  E  A  N  S  E  V  I  G  R  O  F  O
```

4 □ **Pray.** □ **Read Colossians 3:15-17.** □ **Think about what you read using the three keys on the inside front cover.**
Read only the capital letters to find out what Paul said to do.

pLanETiTsHEmPEnACtETsHAlToJEmStUrSCiHeRISeToGIyVEtSRUbLEtINoYO

nURnsHEpAtRaTeS

5 □ **Pray.** □ **Read Colossians 3:18-4:1.** □ **Think about what you read using the three keys on the inside front cover.**
Connect the dots to see what Paul said Christians should work with.

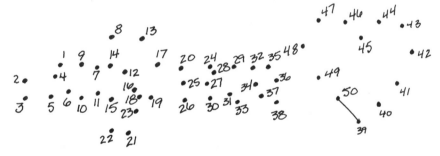

▶ □ **Weekend Review**
Recite your memory verse to an adult. This week, make a poster telling things you are thankful to God for. Ask your family and friends to add to it, also. Then hang it in your room.

1 ☐ **Pray.** ☐ **Read Jeremiah 1:1-5.** ☐ **Think about what you read using the three keys on the inside front cover.**
Do the puzzle about the prophet Jeremiah.

The ____ *(5 Across)* of the Lord came to ____ *(4 Across)*, one of the ____ *(1 Down)* from the territory of ____ *(7 Across)*. This happened when ____ *(8 Across)* was ____ *(2 Down)* of Judah. Later, the ____ *(3 Down)* of Jerusalem were taken captive. God said to Jeremiah, "____ *(6 Across)* I made you in your mother's body, I knew you. Before you were ____ *(6 Down)*, I chose you to be a ____ *(3 Across)*."

2 ☐ **Pray.** ☐ **Read Jeremiah 1:6-10.** ☐ **Think about what you read using the three keys on the inside front cover.**
Mark the statements *T* for *True* or *F* for *False.*

____ Jeremiah thought he was too young to be a prophet.

____ God agreed that Jeremiah was too young.

____ God told Jeremiah not to be afraid of anyone.

____ God told Jeremiah he would rescue him.

____ God touched Jeremiah's ears so he would hear better.

____ God told Jeremiah he was putting his words in his mouth.

____ God put Jeremiah in charge of writing a book.

3 ☐ **Pray.** ☐ **Read Jeremiah 1:11-14.** ☐ **Think about what you read using the three keys on the inside front cover.**
Fill in the letters to see what the boiling pot that Jeremiah saw showed.

DISASTER WOULD BE POURED
OUT ON THE PEOPLE OF JUDAH

4 ☐ **Pray.** ☐ **Read Jeremiah 1:15-16.** ☐ **Think about what you read using the three keys on the inside front cover.**
Use the code to find out why the people of Judah would be attacked.

1	2	3	4	5	6	7	8	9	10	11	12	13	14	15	16	17	18	19	20	21	22	23	24	25	26
a	b	c	d	e	f	g	h	i	j	k	l	m	n	o	p	q	r	s	t	u	v	w	x	y	z

2 5 3 1 21 19 5   20 8 5 25   20 21 18 14 5 4   6 18 15 13   7 15 4

1 14 4   23 15 18 19 8 9 16 5 4   9 4 15 12 19

5 ☐ **Pray.** ☐ **Read Jeremiah 1:17-19.** ☐ **Think about what you read using the three keys on the inside front cover.**

Use the code to find out what God said to Jeremiah.

▶▶	→	➜	→	➡	▮	→	↔	➡	⟫	▶	➡	➡	⟫	➤	◀▦	⬅
A	C	D	E	F	G	H	I	L	M	N	O	P	R	S	T	U

_____ be _____ of the _____.
➡ ➡ ▶ ◀▦   ▶▶ ➡ ⟫ ▶▶ ↔ ➡   ➡ ➡ ➡ ➡ ➡ ➡

They will _____ you, but I _____ with you and I will
         ➡ ↔ ▮ → ◀▦   ▶▶ ⟫

_____ you.
⟫ ➡ ➤ → ⬅ ➡

▶ ☐ **Weekend Review**

Recite your memory verse to an adult. With friends, think of ways someone your age can share God's Word with others, such as by reading Bible stories to children. List ideas in your notebook, and choose one to do this week.

WEEK 46   ☐ Memorize: Daniel 1:17

1 ☐ **Pray.** ☐ **Read Daniel 1:1-7.** ☐ **Think about what you read using the three keys on the inside front cover.**

Use the code to find out why Daniel was taken to King Nebuchadnezzar's house.

Z	Y	X	W	V	U	T	S	R	Q	P	O	N	M	L	K	J	I	H	G	F	E	D	C	B	A
A	B	C	D	E	F	G	H	I	J	K	L	M	N	O	P	Q	R	S	T	U	V	W	X	Y	Z

_____

GL YV GIZRMVW ULI GSV PRMT'H HVIERXV

2 ☐ **Pray.** ☐ **Read Daniel 1:8-14.** ☐ **Think about what you read using the three keys on the inside front cover.**

Write the first letter of each object to see what Daniel asked to eat.

___ ___ ___ ___ ___ ___ ___ ___

___ ___ ___ & ___ ___ ___ ___ ___

3 ☐ **Pray.** ☐ **Read Daniel 1:15-21.** ☐ **Think about what you read using the three keys on the inside front cover.**

Use the code to find out what God gave Daniel.

A	D	E		N	O	R
F	G	I		S	T	U
K	L	M		V	W	space

(coded message in pigpen-style symbols)

4 ☐ **Pray.** ☐ **Read Daniel 2:1-6.** ☐ **Think about what you read using the three keys on the inside front cover.**

To find out what King Nebuchadnezzar told his wise men, first read the darker words left to right and then the lighter ones right to left.

Tell pieces **me** to **my** cut **dream** you & have **tell** I'll me don't **what** you **it** if **means**

5 ☐ **Pray.** ☐ **Read Daniel 2:7-16.** ☐ **Think about what you read using the three keys on the inside front cover.**

Put the number of the statements in the correct speech balloons.

1) "It's too hard! No one can do that!"   2) "All right, I will."   3) "Kill them all!"
4) "Please tell us your dream."   5) "O king, give me more time."   6) "No. You're just trying to get more time."

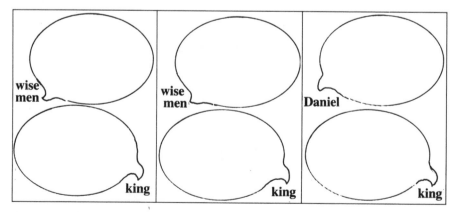

wise men / king
wise men / king
Daniel / king

☐ **Weekend Review**

Recite your memory verse to an adult. This week, help plan, shop for, and cook a healthy snack or meal for your family. Write what you did in your notebook.

1 ☐ **Pray.** ☐ **Read Daniel 2:19-23.** ☐ **Think about what you read using the three keys on the inside front cover.**
Unscramble the words to see what happened when Daniel and his friends prayed.

God **pinedaxel** _____ the **yesmtry** _____ of the

king's **mared** _____ to Daniel in a **novisi** _____ during the

thing _____.

2 ☐ **Pray.** ☐ **Read Daniel 2:24-28.** ☐ **Think about what you read using the three keys on the inside front cover.**
Use the code to see what Daniel said when asked if he could explain the dream.

★	☆	✱	✲	☆	✳	❖	◇	✛	◉	✳	☆	✵
B	C	D	G	H	L	N	P	R	S	T	V	X

__ o __ e __ __ o __ __ a __ e __ __ __ __ __ a i __
❖   ◇ ✛ ◉   ❖   ☆   ❖   ✵ ◇ ☆   ❖

i __, __ u __ __ o __ i __ __ e a __ e __ __ a __.
★   ★ ✱ ✲ ✳   ❖   ☆   ☆ ❖ ☆   ❖

3 ☐ **Pray.** ☐ **Read Daniel 2:29-35.** ☐ **Think about what you read using the three keys on the inside front cover.**
Search for words from King Nebuchadnezzar's dream.

statue	belly	rock	T C H A F F O R E V L I S U N S
head	bronze	smashed	S T A Y E A R S U D Z S A L E T
gold	legs	pieces	E R A L E N I A T N U O M S E A
chest	iron	chaff	H L U L L S T O A I K H E R D T
arms	feet	wind	C A D E H S A M S W A C T L A U
silver	clay	mountain	U P G B R O N Z E T I R O N E E
			T S E C E I P T E E F G N R H I

4 ☐ **Pray.** ☐ **Read Daniel 2:36-43.** ☐ **Think about what you read using the three keys on the inside front cover.**
Match parts of the statue to what Daniel said they stood for in the king's dream.

a third kingdom that will rule the whole earth

a kingdom from across the sea

King Herod

King Nebuchadnezzar

a fifth kingdom that will crumble

a second kingdom, not as great as Nebuchadnezzar's

a fourth kingdom, strong but divided

5 ☐ **Pray.** ☐ **Read Daniel 2:44-49.** ☐ **Think about what you read using the three keys on the inside front cover.**

Separate the letters into words to see what King Nebuchadnezzar told Daniel.

SurelyyourGodistheGodofgods,theLordofkings,andonewhoshowswhat secretthingsmean.

▶ ☐ **Weekend Review**

Recite your memory verse to an adult. This week, help a younger child with reading or a hard school subject. Write the child's name in your notebook.

WEEK 48 ☐ Memorize: Daniel 6:27

1 ☐ **Pray.** ☐ **Read Daniel 6:1-9.** ☐ **Think about what you read using the three keys on the inside front cover.**

Cross out the capital letters to read the 30-day law of King Darius.

OwhoPeverYpArayEstoPanDyoUneeDxceLpUtOtheNkinDgOwiTAllbeAthErowE ntoNUtheRliPonIs

2 ☐ **Pray.** ☐ **Read Daniel 6:10-14.** ☐ **Think about what you read using the three keys on the inside front cover.**

Write the missing letter of the alphabet on each line to find out what Daniel did when he learned about the king's law.

A B C D E F G H I J K L M N O Q R S T U V W X Y Z   _____

A B C D E F G H I J K L M N O P Q S T U V W X Y Z   _____

B C D E F G H I J K L M N O P Q R S T U V W X Y Z   _____

A B C D E F G H I J K L M N O P Q R S T U V W X Z   _____

A B C D F G H I J K L M N O P Q R S T U V W X Y Z   _____

A B C E F G H I J K L M N O P Q R S T U V W X Y Z   _____

B C D E F G H I J K L M N O P Q R S T U V W X Y Z   _____

A B C D E F G H I J K L M N O P Q R T U V W X Y Z   _____

A B C D E F G H I J K L M N O P Q R S T V W X Y Z   _____

A B C D E F G H I J K L M N O P Q R T U V W X Y Z   _____

A B C D E F G H I J K L M N O P Q R S T V W X Y Z   _____

B C D E F G H I J K L M N O P Q R S T U V W X Y Z   _____

A B C D E F G H I J K M N O P Q R S T U V W X Y Z   _____

3

☐ **Pray.** ☐ **Read Daniel 6:15-18.** ☐ **Think about what you read using the three keys on the inside front cover.**

Use the code to find out what the king said to Daniel who was in the lions' den.

¶	𝄪	▜	ℭ	6	▟
A	E	I	O	U	space

M __ y __ y __ __ r G __ d , __ wh __ m __ y __ __ __ __ __
   ¶   ▟   ℭ 6   ▟   ℭ   ▟   ℭ   ▟   ℭ 6 ▟

s __ r v __ __ __ __ l l __ t h __ __ __ __ t __ m __ , __ s __ v __
 𝄪   𝄪 ▟ ¶   ▟   𝄪 ▟   ▜   𝄪   ▟   ¶   𝄪

__ y __ __ __ !
▟   ℭ 6

4

☐ **Pray.** ☐ **Read Daniel 6:19-24.** ☐ **Think about what you read using the three keys on the inside front cover.**

To find out what King Darius asked and what Daniel answered, read the light words left to right and then the dark words right to left.

Has **mouths** your **lions'** God **the** been **shut** able **angel** to **his** save **yes** you?

☐ **Pray.** ☐ **Read Daniel 6:25-28.** ☐ **Think about what you read using the three keys on the inside front cover.**

Number the pieces from King Darius' letter in the correct order.

☐ He saved Daniel from the lions.

☐ He rescues and saves people.

☐ His kingdom will last forever.

☐ He is the living God.

☐ Everyone must respect Daniel's God.

▶ ☐ **Weekend Review**

Recite your memory verse to an adult. This week, find out about people in other parts of the world who suffer because of their faith in God. Mark their country on a world map, record it in your notebook, and pray for them regularly.

1

☐ **Pray.**   ☐ **Read 2 Timothy 1:1-12.**   ☐ **Think about what you read using the three keys on the inside front cover.**

Use the code to find out what the Apostle Paul said God gave us.

0	1	2	3	4	5	6	7	8	9	10	11	12	13	14	15	16	17
space	A	C	D	E	F	G	I	L	N	O	P	R	S	T	U	V	W

1 0 13 11 7 12 7 14 0 10 5 0 8 10 16 4 0 1 9 3 0 11 10 17 4 12 0

1 9 3 0 13 4 8 5 2 10 9 14 12 10 8

2

☐ **Pray.**   ☐ **Read 2 Timothy 1:13-18.**   ☐ **Think about what you read using the three keys on the inside front cover.**

To find out what Paul said, read the phrases in the same order as the pattern.

> ✔ # } ¶ † • § @

¶ of true teaching   # you've heard from me   § the Holy Spirit   ✔ Keep what

† and guard it   @ who lives in us   • with help from   } as the pattern

3

☐ **Pray.**   ☐ **Read 2 Timothy 2:1-13.**   ☐ **Think about what you read using the three keys on the inside front cover.**

Use the code to find out what Paul told Timothy to do.

1	ABC 2	DEF 3
GHI 4	JKL 5	MNO 6
PRS 7	TUV 8	WXY 9

2–1 = A
2–2 = B
2–3 = C
3–1 = D
3–2 = E
3–3 = F
etc.

_____ what you've _____ me _____
8-1 3-2 2-1 2-3 4-2   4-2 3-2 2-1 7-2 3-1   7-3 2-1 9-3

to _____ who can _____
7-1 3-2 6-3 7-1 5-3 3-2   8-1 3-2 2-1 2-3 4-2

_____
6-3 8-1 4-2 3-2 7-2 7-3

4

☐ **Pray.**   ☐ **Read 2 Timothy 2:14-19.**   ☐ **Think about what you read using the three keys on the inside front cover.**

Read the capital letters to see what Paul told Timothy to be.

cAWsOReKEyRoWsHOwHAtNoDuLlEtSaTsHEsWORlDOtFooTRUinTanHItNo

TcHEeRpIGHoToWsAY

5 ☐ **Pray.** ☐ **Read 2 Timothy 2:20-26.** ☐ **Think about what you read using the three keys on the inside front cover.**

Check the correct box to show what Paul told Timothy to do.

Yes   No

☐   ☐   Stay away from evil desires.
☐   ☐   Stay away from right living, faith, love, and peace.
☐   ☐   Keep out of foolish and stupid arguments.
☐   ☐   Be kind just to other Christians.
☐   ☐   Be a good teacher.
☐   ☐   Be resentful sometimes.
☐   ☐   Gently teach those who don't agree with you.

▶ ☐ **Weekend Review**

Recite your memory verse to an adult. Think of a Christian adult you know and want to be like. In your notebook, list three ways you could follow his or her Christian example. Choose one to work on this week.

WEEK 50 ☐ **Memorize: 1 Peter 1:15**

1 ☐ **Pray.** ☐ **Read 1 Peter 1:1-5.** ☐ **Think about what you read using the three keys on the inside front cover.**

Do the puzzle that tells what the Apostle Peter wrote to Christians.

To God's ____(2 Down) people: Grace and ____(1 Across) be yours. ____(1 Down) God! In his great ____(5 Across) he's given us ____(11 Across) birth into a ____ (10 Across) hope because Jesus rose from the ____(6 Across). We have an inheritance that can't be destroyed, ____(4 Down), or fade. It's kept in ____(3 Down) for you. God's ____(9 Across) keeps you safe until the coming of ____(7 Across) at the end of ____(8 Down).

2 ☐ **Pray.** ☐ **Read 1 Peter 1:6-12.** ☐ **Think about what you read using the three keys on the inside front cover.**

Cross out each @ to see what Peter said about the believers' troubles.

@t@rou@b@le@sco@me@top@rov@eyo@urf@ait@hi@sre@ala@ndp@ur@e@

3 ☐ **Pray.** ☐ **Read 1 Peter 1:13-16.** ☐ **Think about what you read using the three keys on the inside front cover.**

Use the code to find out what Peter said Christians should do.

A	B	C	D	E	F	G	H	I	J	K	L	M	N	O	P	Q	R	S	T	U	V	W	X	Y	Z	space
26	25	24	23	22	21	20	19	18	17	16	15	14	13	12	11	10	9	8	7	6	5	4	3	2	1	0

_____

25 22 0 19 12 15 2 0 18 13 0 22 5 22 9 2 7 19 18 13 20 0 2 12 6 0 23

_____

12 0 17 6 8 7 0 26 8 0 20 12 23 0 18 8 0 19 12 15 2

4 ☐ **Pray.** ☐ **Read 1 Peter 1:17-21.** ☐ **Think about what you read using the three keys on the inside front cover.**

Use the code to find out what Peter said about Jesus Christ.

A	C	D	E	H	I	L	M	N	O	R	S	T	W
○	⊖	◉	◶	▢	◑	⊝	◫	■	◎	◔	⊕	◖	⊙

You were _____ by the _____ of

_____ who was _____ before the

_____ was _____ .

5 ☐ **Pray.** ☐ **Read 1 Peter 1:22-25.** ☐ **Think about what you read using the three keys on the inside front cover.**

Use the code to find out what Peter said to do.

A	C	D	E	H	L	O	P	R	T	V	Y
♥	♥	♥	♥	♥	♥	♡	♥	♥	♥	♥	♥

_____ _____ _____

_____ from _____ _____

▶ ☐ **Weekend Review**

Recite your memory verse to an adult. On a card, write a favorite verse from this week's Bible readings. Post it where you'll see it often, and say it regularly this week.

1 ☐ **Pray.** ☐ **Read 1 John 3:1-10.** ☐ **Think about what you read using the three keys on the inside front cover.**
Use the code to find out what the Apostle John said about God the Father.

2 ☐ **Pray.** ☐ **Read 1 John 3:11-24.** ☐ **Think about what you read using the three keys on the inside front cover.**
Starting with keyhole #1, read each keyhole and then its matching key to find out an important command from God.

3 ☐ **Pray.** ☐ **Read 1 John 4:1-6.** ☐ **Think about what you read using the three keys on the inside front cover.**
Use the code to find out what John said to Christians.

4 ☐ **Pray.** ☐ **Read 1 John 4:7-21.** ☐ **Think about what you read using the three keys on the inside front cover.**
Read down the columns to find out what John said about love.

since	us	we	each
God	so	should	other
loved	much	love	too

5 ☐ **Pray.** ☐ **Read 1 John 5:1-12.** ☐ **Think about what you read using the three keys on the inside front cover.**

Hold your book up to a mirror to read what John said about God.

GOD HAS GIVEN US ETERNAL LIFE IN HIS SON, JESUS

(shown in mirror writing)

▶ ☐ **Weekend Review**

Recite your memory verse to an adult. In your notebook, list three ways you can show love to each family member. Put check marks by them whenever you do them.

WEEK 52 ☐ **Memorize: Revelation 21:4**

1 ☐ **Pray.** ☐ **Read Revelation 21:1-8.** ☐ **Think about what you read using the three keys on the inside front cover.**

Following the arrows, read every other word from left to right and then from right to left to see what the Apostle John said would happen in heaven.

God *pain* will *or* wipe *crying* away *or* every *death* tear *more* and *no* there *be* will

2 ☐ **Pray.** ☐ **Read Revelation 21:9-21.** ☐ **Think about what you read using the three keys on the inside front cover.**

Search for words from John's vision of the new Jerusalem.

glory	foundation
jewel	apostles
crystal	sapphire
wall	chalcedony
gates	emerald
twelve	onyx
tribes	carnelian
gold	chrysolite
beryl	topaz
jacinth	chrysoprase
pearl	amethyst

```
S O M A N Y N O D E C L A H C A N
E R A P R C A R N E L I A N H T O
E N D O G U M L S E B I R T R X I
R A L S L J E L O A M E T H Y S T
I G A T A A E A M O V E R N S E A
H A R L T C O W R L O G O Y O U D
P T E E S I N O E X O S E A L I N
P E M S Y N O W E L R A E P I T U
A S E E R T T A D S Z A P O T O O
S E A R C H R Y S O P R A S E O F
```

3 ☐ **Pray.** ☐ **Read Revelation 21:22-27.** ☐ **Think about what you read using the three keys on the inside front cover.**

Use the code to find out about the heavenly city of God.

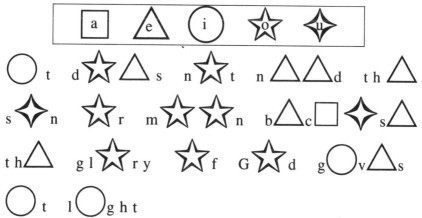

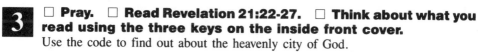

4 ☐ **Pray.** ☐ **Read Revelation 22:1-11.** ☐ **Think about what you read using the three keys on the inside front cover.**

Draw what John saw in his vision of the river of the water of life.

5 ☐ **Pray.** ☐ **Read Revelation 22:12-21.** ☐ **Think about what you read using the three keys on the inside front cover.**

Follow the arrows to read the last words of Jesus in the book of Revelation.

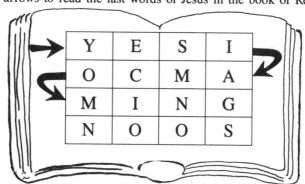

Y	E	S	I
O	C	M	A
M	I	N	G
N	O	O	S

▶ ☐ **Weekend Review**

Recite your memory verse to an adult. In your notebook, write a story or draw a picture of what you want to do in heaven. Then talk with a parent, family member, or friend about what heaven will be like.